The route to your roo

D1537979

When they look back at their formative years, many Indians nostalgically recall the vital part Amar Chitra Katha picture books have played in their lives. It was **ACK – Amar Chitra Katha** – that first gave them a glimpse of their glorious heritage.

Since they were introduced in 1967, there are now **over 400 Amar Chitra Katha** titles to choose from. **Over 100 million copies** have been sold worldwide.

Now the Amar Chitra Katha titles are even more widely available in **1000+ bookstores all across India**. You can also buy all the titles through our online store **www.amarchitrakatha.com**. We provide quick delivery anywhere in the world.

To make it easy for you to locate the titles of your choice from our treasure trove of titles, the books are now arranged in five categories.

Epics and Mythology
Best known stories from the Epics and the Puranas

Indian Classics
Enchanting tales from Indian literature

Fables and Humour
Evergreen folktales, legends and tales of wisdom and humour

Bravehearts
Stirring tales of brave men and women of India

Visionaries
Inspiring tales of thinkers, social reformers and nation builders

Contemporary Classics
The Best of Modern Indian literature

Amar Chitra Katha Pvt Ltd
© Amar Chitra Katha Pvt Ltd, 1972, Reprinted August 2018,
ISBN 978-81-8482-214-4
Published by Amar Chitra Katha Pvt. Ltd., AFL House, 7th Floor,
Lok Bharati Complex,Marol Maroshi Road, Andheri (East), Mumbai - 400059, India.
Printed at M/s Indigo Press (I) Pvt Ltd., Mumbai.
For Consumer Complaints Contact Tel : + 91-2249188881/2
Email: customerservice@ack-media.com

This book is sold subject to the condition that the publication may not be reproduced, stored in a retrieval system (including but not limited to computers, disks, external drives, electronic or digital devices, e-readers, websites), or transmitted in any form or by any means (including but not limited to cyclostyling, photocopying, docutech or other reprographic reproductions, mechanical, recording, electronic, digital versions) without the prior written permission of the publisher, nor be otherwise circulated in any form of binding or cover other than that in which it is published and without a similar condition being imposed on the subsequent purchaser.

The route to your roots

BIRBAL THE CLEVER

Birbal had proved himself to be the most reliable minister at court, time and again. He dispensed justice, dealt diplomatically with other rulers, led military expeditions and composed poetry. In addition, he also rescued Akbar from the dangers of arrogance and unfettered power. Most importantly, he made the Great Mughal laugh.

Script
Meera Ugra

Illustrations
Ram Waeerkar

Editor
Anant Pai

THE PUNISHMENT

AFTER THE DAY'S WORK WAS DONE, AKBAR, THE MUGHAL EMPEROR, LIKED TO PASS A FEW LIGHT-HEARTED MOMENTS WITH HIS COURTIERS. HE OFTEN POSED STRANGE QUESTIONS TO PROVOKE AMUSING REPLIES.

ONE MORNING, AS AKBAR WAS GETTING DRESSED, HIS GRANDSON CAME RUNNING TO HIM.

BABA, BABA, THERE IS SOMETHING BLACK IN YOUR MOUSTACHE! BEND DOWN, AND I WILL TAKE IT OUT!

O...OU...OUCH!

THAT WAS NAUGHTY OF YOU! WHY DID YOU DO IT?

HA! HA! BABA! I FOOLED YOU!

NOW, GO AND PLAY. I'VE GOT WORK TO DO.

1

AKBAR LEFT FOR HIS DARBAR.

AHA, TODAY I HAVE A PROBLEM WHICH WILL BAFFLE EVERYONE — EVEN BIRBAL, MY WITTY MINISTER! HE THINKS HE HAS ALL THE ANSWERS, BUT HE'LL BE FOXED THIS TIME!

SOMEONE PULLED A HAIR FROM MY MOUSTACHE THIS MORNING. I WANT HIM PUNISHED!

CAN ANYONE HERE THINK OF SUITABLE PUNISHMENT FOR THIS DEED?

AFTER A MOMENT'S SHOCKED SILENCE, THERE WAS A CHORUS OF SUGGESTIONS.

THE MAN SHOULD BE FLOGGED A THOUSAND TIMES!

THAT'S TOO MILD! THE SCOUN-DREL SHOULD BE IMPRISONED FOR LIFE!

HANG HIM, JAHANPANAH!

THE EMPEROR TURNED TO BIRBAL.

WHY ARE YOU SO QUIET, BIRBAL? ARE YOU STUCK FOR IDEAS?

NO, JAHAN-PANAH. BUT IT'S A BIT AWKWARD. PERHAPS I SHOULD SPEAK TO YOU IN PRIVATE....

NO, BIRBAL! LET EVERYONE HEAR WHAT YOU HAVE TO SAY.

THE GUILTY PERSON DESERVES ONE LOUD, RESOUNDING KISS!

BIRBAL HAS GONE OUT OF HIS MIND!

WHAT!

AS USUAL, MY CLEVER MINISTER HAS GOT THE BETTER OF ME!

BIRBAL, EXPLAIN YOURSELF. WHY THIS STRANGE PUNISHMENT?

ONLY A CHILD WOULD DARE TO INDULGE IN SUCH A PRANK. AND THAT CHILD COULD ONLY BE YOUR GRAND-SON!

HA! HA! CLEVER BIRBAL!

THE MOST BEAUTIFUL CHILD IN AGRA

AKBAR WAS VERY FOND OF HIS GRANDCHILDREN.

ONCE —

ISN'T PRINCE KHURRAM MORE HANDSOME THAN ANY OTHER CHILD AROUND?

YES, JAHANPANAH!

WITHOUT A DOUBT, JAHANPANAH!

YOU ARE SILENT, BIRBAL? DON'T YOU AGREE WITH ME?

IT IS A DIFFICULT QUESTION, JAHANPANAH. FOR THERE IS NO REAL TEST FOR BEAUTY.

WHY NOT? WHO WOULD CALL A ROSE UGLY OR A CROW BEAUTIFUL?

HMM... YOU HAVE A POINT THERE, JAHANPANAH.

YOU DON'T SEEM CONVINCED. ALL RIGHT, WE'LL HAVE A CONTEST TOMORROW.

EACH OF YOU SHALL BRING ALONG A CHILD. I AM SURE WE WILL THEN BE ABLE TO DECIDE WHICH AMONG THEM IS THE MOST BEAUTIFUL.

THE NEXT DAY, AKBAR FOUND THAT THE NOBLES HAD FOLLOWED HIS INSTRUCTIONS—

HMM. THAT CHILD'S EYES ARE A BIT SMALL FOR HIS FACE. AND THAT ONE THERE LOOKS A BIT TOO FAT.

I STILL THINK MY KHURRAM LOOKS BETTER THAN ALL OF THEM. BUT, BIRBAL, WHY HAVEN'T YOU BROUGHT A CHILD?

JAHANPANAH, I COULD NOT FIND A CHILD WHO IS PERFECT IN EVERY FEATURE. GIVE ME A FEW MORE DAYS.

SOMETIME LATER—

BIRBAL, I AM STILL WAITING. HOW MUCH LONGER WILL YOU TAKE?

MY SEARCH IS STILL ON, JAHANPANAH.

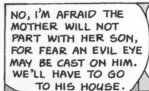

THEN, ONE DAY —

JAHANPANAH, AT LAST I HAVE FOUND THE MOST BEAUTIFUL CHILD IN AGRA.

HAVE YOU BROUGHT IT HERE?

NO, I'M AFRAID THE MOTHER WILL NOT PART WITH HER SON, FOR FEAR AN EVIL EYE MAY BE CAST ON HIM. WE'LL HAVE TO GO TO HIS HOUSE.

ALL RIGHT, I AM VERY CURIOUS TO SEE THIS CHILD. WE WILL DRESS LIKE ORDINARY CITIZENS AND GO.

TAKING ONLY A FEW COMPANIONS WITH THEM, AKBAR AND BIRBAL WENT OUT IN DISGUISE. THEY WALKED FOR A LONG TIME.

HOW MUCH FURTHER IS IT?

WE HAVE COME A LONG WAY. WHERE IS BIRBAL TAKING US TO?

THE HOUSES ARE BEGINNING TO LOOK MORE AND MORE SHABBY AND DIRTY. I HOPE BIRBAL KNOWS WHAT HE IS DOING!

FINALLY, BIRBAL STOPPED.

THAT'S WHERE THE CHILD LIVES, MY LORD. WE'LL WATCH HIM FROM A DISTANCE.

BUT WHERE IS HE, BIRBAL?

WHY, THERE HE IS!

ALL EYES TURNED TOWARDS THE "MOST BEAUTIFUL CHILD IN AGRA".

THAT CHILD! IS THIS ANOTHER OF YOUR PRANKS, BIRBAL? THIS IS THE UGLIEST CHILD I HAVE EVER COME ACROSS!

I BEG OF YOU TO BE A LITTLE MORE PATIENT, JAHANPANAH.

JUST THEN THE CHILD STUMBLED AND FELL.

O....O....A....

HIS MOTHER RUSHED OUT OF THE HUT.

OH—MY CHILD!

SHE PICKED HIM UP AND CARESSED HIM.

MY SWEETHEART, MY ANGEL! MY LOVELY ONE FELL DOWN! I'LL BEAT THE GROUND! HURTING MY MOON SO!

HOW CAN SHE LOVE THIS UGLY CHILD? HE IS UTTERLY REPULSIVE. DON'T YOU THINK SO, FRIEND?

YES, IMAGINE CALLING THE CHILD A MOON! UGH!

THE WOMAN JUMPED UP TO FACE THEM.

WHAT? WHAT DID YOU SAY? JUST SAY IT AGAIN.

WE SPOKE THE TRUTH. THIS CHILD IS...!

BE QUIET! THERE'S NO NEED TO REPEAT SUCH LIES! YOU MUST BE BLIND OR STUPID — GO AND SEARCH ALL OF AGRA AND SEE IF YOU CAN FIND A LOVELIER CHILD. GO AWAY NOW, OR I'LL GIVE YOU A PROPER THRASHING!

THEY BEAT A HASTY RETREAT.

I UNDERSTAND, BIRBAL. EVERY CHILD IS SURPASSINGLY BEAUTIFUL IN THE EYES OF ITS PARENTS...

...OR ITS GRANDPARENTS!

THE WHIM OF A CHILD

EMPEROR AKBAR AND HIS COURTIERS WERE ASSEMBLED IN COURT.

I DON'T SEE BIRBAL HERE TODAY. WHAT COULD HAVE HAPPENED TO HIM?

JUST THEN, BIRBAL CAME IN —

A THOUSAND APOLOGIES, JAHAN-PANAH. I AM INDEED ASHAMED TO HAVE ARRIVED LATE BEFORE YOUR AUGUST PRESENCE.

IT IS ALL RIGHT, BIRBAL. SOMETHING EXTRAORDINARY MUST HAVE DELAYED YOU.

WHEN BIRBAL DIDN'T REPLY, AKBAR PRESSED FURTHER.

WHAT WAS IT, BIRBAL? WHAT MADE YOU SO LATE?

I WAS DETAINED BY...ER...

DETAINED BY WHAT?

IT WAS LIKE THIS, JAHANPANAH — MY SON ... WELL ... YOU SEE ... HE IS ONLY FOUR YEARS OLD. HIS TOY BROKE AND HE WOULDN'T LET ME GO TILL I HAD REPAIRED IT.

SO BIRBAL CAME LATE BECAUSE HE COULDN'T COPE WITH HIS SON! HA! HA!

HA! HA!

BIRBAL MET HIS MATCH TODAY IN A CHILD! HA! HA!

BIRBAL BEATEN BY A MERE CHILD! HA! HA!

EXCUSE ME, JAHANPANAH, BUT SOMETIMES EVEN THE GODS ARE HELPLESS IN THE FACE OF A CHILD'S OBSTINACY.

BUT THAT'S ABSURD! BRING YOUR SON HERE, AND I'LL TACKLE HIM IN NO TIME.

SO BIRBAL'S SON WAS BROUGHT BEFORE THE EMPEROR.

WELL, CHILD, WOULD YOU LIKE TO EAT SOMETHING?

HUZOOR, I WOULD....

YES, YES, GO ON. DON'T HESITATE. WHAT WOULD YOU LIKE TO EAT?

CAN I HAVE SOME SUGAR-CANE? I LIKE IT VERY MUCH.

SOME SUGAR-CANE, CUT INTO PIECES, WAS GIVEN TO THE CHILD.

WHY HAVE YOU CUT IT? I WANT A WHOLE STICK OF SUGAR-CANE.

ALL RIGHT. TAKE THESE PIECES AWAY AND BRING A WHOLE ONE.

NO, NO, I WANT THIS ONE AND NO OTHER!

BUT, YOU JUST SAID YOU WANTED A WHOLE STICK OF SUGAR-CANE.

YES, OF COURSE, I WANT A WHOLE STICK OF SUGAR-CANE! I WANT THIS ONE JOINED TOGETHER AGAIN!

BUT THAT'S IMPOSSIBLE, CHILD. HAVE ANOTHER ONE.

NO! NO! NO! I WANT THIS ONE! WHY DID YOU CUT MY SUGAR-CANE? SOB! SOB! JOIN IT NOW! SOB!

PLEASE ASK FOR ANYTHING ELSE AND YOU SHALL HAVE IT. STOP CRYING. YOU'RE A GOOD BOY, AREN'T YOU?

NO... I DON'T... WANT... ANYTHING ... ELSE ... I... WANT... MY ... SOB!

OH, GOD! I GIVE UP! PLEASE TAKE HIM AWAY!

SOB...SOB...!

YOU WERE RIGHT, BIRBAL. SOMETIMES EVEN A SMALL CHILD CAN GET THE BETTER OF US!

THE MAN WHO BROUGHT ILL LUCK

THE DAY'S WORK IN AKBAR'S PALACE BEGAN VERY EARLY IN THE MORNING.

THERE GOES GULSHAN, THE INAUSPICIOUS ONE. WE HAVE SEEN HIS FACE THE FIRST THING THIS MORNING. WE WILL NOT GET ANY FOOD TODAY.

OR, PERHAPS, A WORSE CALAMITY WILL BEFALL US!

THAT DAY, THE EMPEROR WOKE UP EARLIER THAN USUAL.

IS SOMEONE THERE?

THERE IS NO ONE ELSE AROUND. I DON'T WANT TO BE THE FIRST PERSON HE SEES THIS MORNING BUT....

GULSHAN WENT IN RELUCTANTLY.

JAHANPANAH....

MY SLIPPERS! GIVE ME MY SLIPPERS!

OH! IT'S THAT SERVANT WHOM EVERYONE AVOIDS!

SEND THE OTHER SERVANTS IN TO HELP ME GET DRESSED!

YES, HUZOOR.

A LITTLE LATER —

JAHANPANAH! PRINCE KHURRAM IS VERY ILL AND HAS BEEN CRYING FOR YOU.

I'LL COME AT ONCE!

THE EMPEROR SPENT A FEW ANXIOUS HOURS BY THE CHILD'S BED. THEN —

THANK GOD, THE FEVER HAS COME DOWN!

JAHANPANAH, THE CRISIS IS OVER; YOU SHOULD REST NOW.

AS AKBAR WAS GOING TO HIS CHAMBERS TO HAVE A LATE BREAKFAST —

JAHANPANAH, THE BURMESE AMBASSADOR HAS BEEN WAITING FOR AN AUDIENCE ALL MORNING.

YES, YES, I'LL COME AT ONCE.

LATER, JUST AS AKBAR WAS BIDDING THE AMBASSADOR FAREWELL, A MINISTER APPROACHED.

JAHANPANAH, MAY I HAVE A WORD WITH YOU IN PRIVATE? IT'S EXTREMELY URGENT.

I BRING BAD NEWS. THERE HAS BEEN A REBELLION.

A REBELLION! WE MUST ACT IMMEDIATELY. CALL THE COMMANDER IN CHARGE OF THE AREA!

THEY HELD CONSULTATIONS. IT WAS NEARLY EVENING WHEN THEY FINISHED.

I AM SO TIRED AND I HAVE HAD NOTHING TO EAT ALL DAY!

I'LL HAVE SOME REFRESHMENTS SENT IN IMMEDIATELY, JAHANPANAH.

BUT WHEN AKBAR SAT DOWN TO EAT—

A...AAH! I HAVE A PIERCING PAIN IN THE STOMACH...CALL MY PHYSICIAN!

WITHIN MINUTES, THE PHYSICIAN ARRIVED—

JAHANPANAH, PLEASE DO NOT EAT ANYTHING. YOU CAN DRINK SOME FRUIT JUICE, THOUGH.

A...AH... ALL RIGHT.

WHAT A DAY IT HAS BEEN! CAN GULSHAN HAVE BEEN THE CAUSE OF MY TROUBLES?

TORMENTED BY PAIN, FATIGUE AND HUNGER, AKBAR MADE A RASH DECISION.

SUCH A MAN IS A THREAT TO ALL THOSE AROUND HIM. HE SHOULD NOT LIVE!

THE NEXT DAY, THE WHOLE COURT WAS BUZZING WITH THE NEWS —

THE INAUSPICIOUS ONE IS TO BE EXECUTED!

THAT'S A GOOD THING! I GET VERY WORRIED WHENEVER I SEE GULSHAN.

BUT BIRBAL WAS DISTURBED.

I MUST MAKE THE EMPEROR SEE REASON. THE POOR MAN HAS COMMITTED NO CRIME!

JAHANPANAH, I WANT TO APPEAL TO YOU ON GULSHAN'S BEHALF. TO PROVE HIS INNOCENCE, CAN I ASK HIM A FEW QUESTIONS IN YOUR PRESENCE?

ALL RIGHT, BIRBAL. GO AHEAD.

GULSHAN WAS CALLED IN.

TELL ME, GULSHAN, WHOM DID YOU MEET YESTERDAY WHEN YOU STARTED YOUR DAILY DUTIES IN THE MORNING?

THERE WAS NO ONE AROUND, HUZOOR, I DID NOT MEET ANYONE.

THEN WHOM DID YOU SEE FIRST OF ALL, GULSHAN?

I SAW EMPEROR AKBAR.

JAHANPANAH, YOU CLAIM THE SIGHT OF THIS MAN'S FACE RESULTED IN YOUR TROUBLES YESTERDAY...

... BUT WHAT IF HE WERE TO CLAIM THAT THE SIGHT OF YOUR FACE WILL CAUSE THE LOSS OF HIS LIFE!

WHOSE FATE IS WORSE AND WHO IS RESPONSIBLE?

YOU ARE RIGHT. I WAS LOOKING AT IT ONLY FROM MY POINT OF VIEW.

YOU HAVE SAVED ME FROM PUNISHING AN INNOCENT PERSON, BIRBAL. RELEASE THE POOR MAN.

THE OBEDIENT HUSBAND

ONE DAY, AKBAR AND BIRBAL WERE GOING AROUND THE TOWN IN DISGUISE.

THEY HEARD A WOMAN LOUDLY SCOLDING HER HUSBAND.

YOU FOOL! YOU GOOD-FOR-NOTHING OAF! GO AWAY AND DON'T COME BACK, TILL YOU'VE DONE THE WORK.

WHY DO YOU THINK SUCH A STRONG, HEFTY MAN WOULD TAKE THOSE WORDS SO MEEKLY?

WIVES GENERALLY ORDER THEIR HUSBANDS AROUND, JAHANPANAH. THAT'S MARRIAGE FOR YOU.

AKBAR WAS NOT CONVINCED. HE DECIDED TO CONDUCT AN EXPERIMENT. SO THE NEXT DAY, HE SUMMONED ALL THE MARRIED MEN OF AGRA.

THE EMPEROR WANTS TO KNOW HOW MANY MEN IN THIS GATHERING OBEY THEIR WIVES' COMMANDS.

THOSE WHO DO WILL PLEASE GO TO THE RIGHT, AND THOSE WHO DO NOT, WILL GO TO THE LEFT.

THERE WAS A SCRAMBLE.

THEN A FEW MOMENTS LATER, EVERYONE HAD GONE TOWARDS THE RIGHT, EXCEPT FOR ONE SOLITARY PERSON.

AH! THERE IS AT LEAST ONE WISE MAN WHO DOES NOT FOLLOW HIS WIFE'S COMMANDS. I MUST REWARD HIM!

WAIT, JAHANPANAH! PLEASE LET ME ASK HIM ONE QUESTION FIRST.

THE EMPEROR IS PLEASED WITH YOU, YOUNG MAN. AND HE WANTS TO HONOUR YOU. BUT, FIRST, YOU MUST ANSWER ONE QUESTION...

... TELL ME, WHY DID YOU GO TO THE LEFT?

WELL... SIR... BECAUSE MY WIFE HAD TOLD ME TO KEEP AWAY FROM THE CROWDS. AND SO...

... WHEN EVERYONE MOVED TO THE RIGHT I REMEMBERED HER INSTRUCTIONS AND MOVED TO THE LEFT!

HA! HA!

HA! HA!

THE SEARCH FOR BIRBAL

THERE WERE OCCASIONS WHEN AKBAR GOT ANGRY WITH BIRBAL. ONE DAY, AKBAR BANISHED HIM FROM HIS COURT.

BIRBAL WENT HOME, AND WONDERED WHAT HE SHOULD DO NEXT.

IF I STAY HERE, THE EMPEROR MAY GIVE ME SOME HEAVIER PUNISHMENT. FOR THERE ARE MANY WHO ARE WAITING FOR AN OPPORTUNITY TO POISON HIS MIND AGAINST ME.

BUT IF I GO AWAY TO MY JAGIR, HE CAN EASILY RECALL ME. I MUST GO TO AN UNKNOWN PLACE, SO THAT HE WILL REALLY MISS ME.

AFTER A FEW WEEKS —

LIFE IS SO DULL WITHOUT BIRBAL'S QUICK WIT. HE WAS SO HONEST AND FEARLESS.

HE SENT HIS MESSENGERS TO LOOK FOR BIRBAL. BUT —

JAHANPANAH, WE HAVE LOOKED EVERY-WHERE. NO ONE KNOWS WHERE HE IS.

HMM. HE IS NEITHER IN AGRA NOR IN HIS JAGIR! HE MUST BE HIDING IN SOME OUT-OF-THE-WAY VILLAGE!

I MUST THINK OF A NOVEL WAY TO LOCATE HIM.

A FEW DAYS LATER, ALL THE VILLAGE CHIEFS RECEIVED A ROYAL COMMAND—

THE EMPEROR COMMANDS OUR PRESENCE IN AGRA WITHIN FIFTEEN DAYS. AS WE GO THERE, WE MUST WALK PARTLY IN THE SHADE AND PARTLY IN THE SUN.

WHAT AN EXTRAORDINARY COMMAND! HOW CAN ONE DO THAT?

FIFTEEN DAYS LATER, AKBAR WATCHED THE CHIEFS ARRIVING.

ONE OF THEM WAS WALKING VERY CONFIDENTLY.

AHA! HE IS ACTUALLY WALKING PARTLY IN THE SHADE AND PARTLY IN THE SUN!

BRING THAT MAN HERE!

HOW DID YOU THINK OF THIS IDEA? SPEAK THE TRUTH.

JAHANPANAH, A FEW WEEKS AGO, A FRIEND OF A FRIEND OF MINE ARRIVED AT MY VILLAGE. HE IS MY GUEST. IT WAS HIS IDEA.

WHAT IS HIS NAME? SPEAK UP WITHOUT FEAR AND YOU WILL BE REWARDED.

WELL...MY LORD ...HIS NAME IS BIRBAL. BUT...HE SAID THAT SINCE HE WAS IN ROYAL DISFAVOUR....

DON'T WORRY ABOUT THAT. I PARDONED HIM LONG AGO. TELL HIM TO RETURN TO COURT.

AND BIRBAL REGAINED HIS PLACE IN AKBAR'S COURT.

THE LINGUIST

ONE DAY, A STRANGER ARRIVED AT AKBAR'S COURT.

JAHANPANAH, I CAN SPEAK PERSIAN, ARABIC, SANSKRIT, CHINESE AND LATIN.

WHERE HAVE YOU COME FROM, STRANGER?

THEY SAY A MAN'S LANGUAGE IS THE SUREST CLUE TO HIS ORIGIN. CAN THE WISE MEN OF YOUR COURT ANSWER YOUR QUESTION?

SEVERAL SCHOLARS QUESTIONED HIM IN VARIOUS LANGUAGES—

JAHANPANAH, HE SPEAKS MANY LANGUAGES FLUENTLY!

AND HIS DICTION AND COMMAND OVER EACH LANGUAGE IS PERFECT.

AKBAR TURNED TO BIRBAL —

WELL, BIRBAL, YOU'VE BEEN DEEP IN THOUGHT. SURELY YOU'VE DISCOVERED WHERE THIS MAN HAILS FROM?

I NEED A LITTLE MORE TIME, JAHANPANAH. PERHAPS BY TOMORROW I'LL BE ABLE TO TELL YOU.

LATER, BIRBAL CALLED A SERVANT AND GAVE HIM INSTRUCTIONS.

FOLLOW THAT STRANGER AND FIND OUT WHERE HE IS STAYING. THEN TONIGHT....

THAT NIGHT, A SHADOWY FIGURE QUIETLY SLIPPED INTO THE ROOM WHERE THE STRANGER WAS SLEEPING ...

...QUICKLY SPRINKLED A LITTLE WATER ON THE MAN...

...AND GLIDED OUT AS QUIETLY AS IT HAD COME. THE MAN WOKE UP WITH A START.

O!*!*!*!

THE NEXT DAY IN COURT —

THE STRANGER COMES FROM GUJARAT, JAHANPANAH.

OH! HOW DID HE GUESS?

WELL, IS IT TRUE, STRANGER?

Y... YES, JAHAN-PANAH. BUT HOW DID HE FIND OUT?

THE WHOLE COURT WAS EAGER TO HEAR THE ANSWER. BIRBAL EXPLAINED —

JAHANPANAH, I TOLD MY SERVANT TO SPRINKLE A LITTLE WATER ON OUR VISITOR AS HE SLEPT, AND I WAITED OUTSIDE, LISTENING CLOSELY.

IN MOMENTS OF PAIN, SURPRISE OR ANGER, A MAN USES HIS MOTHER-TONGUE. AND SO, WHEN I FOUND HIM MUMBLING IN GUJARATI, THE MYSTERY WAS SOLVED!

THE GREATER FOOL

ONCE AKBAR HAD ASKED BIRBAL TO MAKE A LIST OF FOOLS. SO BIRBAL WENT THROUGH THE STREETS OF AGRA LOOKING FOR FOOLS.

MEANWHILE, A MERCHANT ARRIVED AT THE COURT AND BOWED LOW BEFORE AKBAR.

YOUR MAJESTY, I SELL HORSES OF THE FINEST BREED. I HAVE BROUGHT ONE AS A SAMPLE. IT WOULD GIVE ME GOOD FORTUNE IF YOU JUST GAVE IT A GLANCE.

HORSES WERE AKBAR'S WEAKNESS. HE HAD THOUSANDS OF THEM IN HIS STABLE, BUT THE PROSPECT OF BUYING SOME MORE FINE STEEDS ALWAYS APPEALED TO HIM. HE INSPECTED THE HORSE PERSONALLY.

THAT IS A FINE SPECIMEN!

YOUR MAJESTY, I HAVE A HUNDRED SUCH HORSES. WOULD YOU LIKE TO BUY ALL OF THEM?

YES! WHEN CAN YOU BRING THEM?

JAHANPANAH, BUT FOR THE HEAVY EXPENSE I WOULD HAVE BROUGHT THEM WITH ME.

GIVE ME A LAKH OF GOLD COINS AND I WILL COME BACK WITH THEM IN A FORTNIGHT.

ONE LAKH OF GOLD COINS! OH, ALL RIGHT.

THE TREASURER WAS SUMMONED AND, RECEIVING THE MONEY, THE MERCHANT LEFT.

AH! THERE IS BIRBAL! I MUST SHOW HIM THIS FINE HORSE!

LOOK AT THIS FINE HORSE, BIRBAL! I HAVE JUST GIVEN THE MERCHANT A LAKH OF GOLD COINS FOR A HUNDRED SUCH HORSES.

YOU MEAN... YOU GAVE HIM THAT AMOUNT IN ADVANCE?

YES, OF COURSE! THE HORSES ARE CHEAP EVEN AT THAT PRICE. LET'S GO IN, NOW.

BUT, JAHANPANAH, DID THE MAN HAVE SUITABLE REFERENCES? OR DO YOU KNOW HIS ADDRESS? DID SOMEONE AT THE COURT STAND GUARANTEE FOR HIM?

NO...NO! BUT HE LOOKED HONEST ENOUGH. HE WILL COME BACK, BIRBAL. TELL ME NOW, HOW IS THE LIST OF FOOLS COMING ALONG?

IT IS ALMOST READY, JAHANPANAH. I HAVE JUST ONE MORE NAME TO ADD TO IT.

WELL, LET ME SEE IT THEN.

I'LL SHOW IT TO YOU IN A MOMENT.

BIRBAL STEPPED ASIDE TO WRITE ONE MORE NAME AND CAME BACK ALMOST IMMEDIATELY.

HERE IT IS, JAHANPANAH.

WHAT IS THIS? HOW DARE YOU, BIRBAL! WHY IS MY NAME ON THIS LIST?

I BEG YOUR PARDON, JAHANPANAH. BUT YOU HAVE JUST GIVEN AN UNKNOWN PERSON A LAKH OF GOLD COINS. WHAT ELSE CAN I CALL IT BUT AN ACT OF FOOLISHNESS?

BUT...HOW ARE YOU SO SURE? THE MATTER IS NOT CLOSED YET. WHAT IF HE COMES BACK WITHIN A FORTNIGHT WITH THE HORSES?

IN THAT CASE, I'LL TAKE OFF YOUR NAME FROM THE TOP OF THE LIST, JAHANPANAH...

...AND WRITE HIS NAME THERE!

AKBAR COULDN'T HELP LAUGHING. AND ONCE MORE BIRBAL HAD GOT AWAY WITH A CHEEKY ANSWER.

THOSE WHO CANNOT SEE

ONCE AKBAR HAD A CENSUS OF BLIND MEN TAKEN. BIRBAL WAS WITH HIM WHEN HE RECEIVED THE REPORT.

BIRBAL, THE BEGUM WANTS TO GIVE ALMS TO ALL THE BLIND PERSONS IN THE CITY. IT WAS EASY TO MAKE A LIST OF THEM BECAUSE THEY ARE SO FEW!

BUT, JAHANPANAH, THOSE WHO CANNOT SEE ARE MORE IN NUMBER THAN THOSE WHO CAN SEE!

DON'T BE SILLY, BIRBAL. MY MEN HAVE MADE A CAREFUL CHECK, AND YOU ARE WRONG.

THEY FORGOT TO INCLUDE THOSE WHO HAVE SIGHT AND YET CANNOT SEE, JAHANPANAH.

LOOK, BIRBAL, LET'S HAVE NO MORE OF YOUR JOKES.

YOU'LL SEE WHAT I MEAN, QUITE SOON, JAHANPANAH. JUST GIVE ME A FEW DAYS.

A FEW DAYS LATER, IN THE CITY'S MAIN STREET—

WHAT A CURIOUS SIGHT! WHAT IS HAPPENING HERE?

OH! IT'S BIRBAL!

HE'S UP TO SOME NEW GAME. LET'S GO NEARER AND SEE.

BIRBAL, WHAT ARE YOU DOING?

YES, WHAT IS THIS, BIRBAL?

TELL US!

START WRITING DOWN. NUMBER ONE, TWO, THREE...

SOON, MORE AND MORE CURIOUS PEOPLE ARRIVED.

WHAT ARE YOU DOING BIRBAL?

WHAT ARE YOU UP TO?

BIRBAL PAID NO ATTENTION, BUT WENT ON DICTATING NUMBERS TO HIS CLERK.

SEVENTY-TWO, SEVENTY-THREE, SEVENTY-FOUR....

HAS HE GONE CRAZY?

LOOKS LIKE IT! POOR MAN!

AFTER SOME TIME, EMPEROR AKBAR PASSED BY. HE, TOO, STOPPED.

BIRBAL, WHAT IS ALL THIS! WHAT ARE YOU DOING?

IGNORING THE EMPEROR, BIRBAL AGAIN INSTRUCTED HIS CLERK—

THAT WILL BE TWO HUNDRED AND FIFTY!

BIRBAL! WHAT SORT OF AN ANSWER IS THIS?

I AM STRINGING A CHARPOY, JAHANPANAH. AND I AM ALSO MAKING A LIST.

LIST OF WHAT?

A LIST OF BLIND PERSONS, JAHANPANAH.

TODAY TWO HUNDRED AND FIFTY MEN ASKED ME WHAT I WAS DOING, THOUGH I WAS WORKING IN BROAD DAYLIGHT.

OH, I SEE! BUT... WHAT'S THIS! YOU'VE GOT MY NAME HERE TOO!

YOU WERE THE LAST OF THOSE WHO ASKED ME WHAT I WAS DOING, JAHANPANAH!

HA! HA! HA! ALWAYS A WAG, EH, BIRBAL?

WHO IS GREATER?

WHEN BIRBAL ARRIVED AT COURT ONE DAY—

WATCH OUT, BIRBAL. THE KING IS IN A QUIZZING MOOD TODAY.

WHO IS GREATER, INDRA OR I?

INDRA, THE RAIN GOD, YOUR MAJESTY.

HOW DARE YOU CALL ANYONE GREATER THAN ME?

I BEG YOUR PARDON, YOUR MAJESTY.

YOU ARE GREATER THAN INDRA, O KING.

THEN YOU MUST PROVE IT!

JUST THEN BIRBAL WALKED IN—

THAT'S EASY YOUR MAJESTY!

EXPLAIN, BIRBAL.

BRAHMA THE CREATOR ALSO FACED THE SAME PROBLEM. SO HE ORDERED TWO IMAGES TO BE MADE, ONE OF YOU AND ONE OF LORD INDRA.

THEN HE ORDERED THESE TO BE PLACED ON THE CELESTIAL BALANCE TO SEE WHICH WAS GREATER.

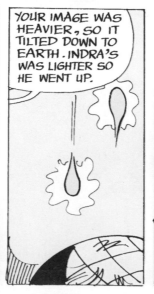

YOUR IMAGE WAS HEAVIER, SO IT TILTED DOWN TO EARTH. INDRA'S WAS LIGHTER SO HE WENT UP.

AS A RESULT, INDRA GOT TO RULE THE HEAVENS WHILE YOU WERE MADE THE MONARCH OF THE EARTH.

HA! HA! WELL SAID, BIRBAL.

BIRBAL
THE GENIUS
WIT AND WISDOM AT AKBAR'S COURT

The route to your roots

BIRBAL
THE GENIUS

It takes a wise man to recognise another's wisdom. While his courtiers were jealous of Birbal, the emperor was quick to notice his agile mind. While the two men loathed hypocrisy and deceit, they also relished a good joke.

Script
Dev Nadkarni

Illustrations
Ram Waeerkar

Editor
Anant Pai

HOW AKBAR MET BIRBAL

AKBAR OFTEN WANDERED INCOGNITO THROUGH THE STREETS OF AGRA TO SEE FOR HIMSELF WHAT WENT ON IN HIS EMPIRE.

ON ONE SUCH OCCASION —

WHAT'S GOING ON HERE?

LISTEN, O CITIZENS OF AGRA, LISTEN! YOU ARE ABOUT TO WITNESS THE GREATEST BAHURUPEE* ON EARTH!

THIS IS INTERESTING!

OUR FIRST ITEM...

THE BULLOCK!

* (LITERALLY "MANY FORMS") ONE WHO SPECIALISES IN THE ART OF DISGUISE

CALM DOWN, CALM DOWN.

AREN'T YOU HUNGRY? WON'T YOU EAT SOMETHING?

WHAT A PERFECT DISGUISE!

WAH–WAH!

THIS TROUPE SEEMS TO HAVE PERFECTED THE ART.

IT DESERVES ALL THESE CHEERS AND MORE.

BUT THAT YOUNG MAN DOESN'T SEEM TO BE IMPRESSED.

AKBAR COULDN'T HELP NOTICING THE YOUNG MAN WHO STOOD UNMOVED.

WHEN THE SHOW WAS OVER AND THE APPLAUSE HAD DIED DOWN, THE YOUNG MAN PICKED UP A STONE...

...AND HURLED IT AT THE BULL.

THAT WAS PERFECT! WAH-WAH, WHAT A GREAT SHOW!

?

THE LAD IS OUT OF HIS SENSES!

THERE'S NO DOUBT ABOUT IT.

I'M NOT SO SURE.

LISTEN, YOUNG MAN...

YES?

WILL YOU EXPLAIN WHY YOU THREW A STONE AT THAT BULL AND THEN CLAPPED.

WELL, IT'S LIKE THIS, SIR. ANYONE WITH A LITTLE BIT OF SKILL CAN DISGUISE HIMSELF WELL.

BUT ONLY A FEW CAN PERFECT THAT DISGUISE DOWN TO THE REFLEX ACTIONS. WHEN THE STONE I THREW HIT THE "BULL", IT ACTUALLY TWITCHED ITS SKIN EXACTLY AS A REAL BULL IN PAIN WOULD.

I SEE. WAS THAT WHY YOU CLAPPED SO LOUD AND LONG?

YES.

WELL, YOU SEEM TO BE AN INTELLIGENT YOUNG MAN. WHAT'S YOUR NAME?

BIRBAL, SIR.

BIRBAL, WILL YOU COME WITH ME AND WORK FOR ME?

OF COURSE, JAHANPANAH! HOW COULD I REFUSE A ROYAL ORDER!

BUT... BUT...

...HOW DID YOU KNOW I WAS...

YOUR DISGUISE IS PERFECT, JAHANPANAH. BUT...

...THE WAY YOU SPOKE AND YOUR REGAL BEARING GAVE YOU AWAY.

AND THAT IS HOW BIRBAL CAME TO BE ONE OF THE NINE GEMS OF AKBAR'S COURT.

THE WASHERMAN AND THE POTTER

ON THE OUTSKIRTS OF AGRA LIVED A POTTER AND A WASHERMAN.

ONE DAY—

ALL MY DAY'S LABOUR WASTED!

GET OUT OF HERE, YOU STUPID BEAST.

HEE... HAW HEE... HAW

HEY, STOP IT! THAT'S MY DONKEY.

SO WHAT? IT HAS BROKEN MY BEST POTS.

IS THAT ALL?

I'LL PAY FOR THE BROKEN POTS.

HERE'S THE MONEY.

NOW THERE'S A FAIR NEIGHBOUR FOR YOU!

A TRUE GENTLEMAN IF I'VE SEEN ONE.

SO HE WAS OUT TO BELITTLE ME BEFORE EVERYONE! HUMPH! I'LL GET EVEN WITH THE FELLOW.

THE NEXT MORNING AT AKBAR'S COURT—

JAHANPANAH, A FRIEND OF MINE HAS JUST RETURNED FROM PERSIA. HE SAYS YOU ARE FAMOUS IN THAT LAND. HE SAYS THE PEOPLE THERE HOLD YOU IN HIGH ESTEEM.

HOWEVER...

WHAT IS IT, MY MAN?

THE PEOPLE OF PERSIA SEEM TO THINK POORLY OF THE ROYAL ELEPHANTS OF AGRA.

OUR ELEPHANTS?

YES. THEY SAY THEY'RE TOO GREY AND DIRTY.

THEY SAY THAT'S NOT HOW ROYAL ELEPHANTS SHOULD BE.

HMM...

THE KING OF PERSIA MAINTAINS A STABLE FULL OF SPARKLING WHITE ELEPHANTS.

OH YES?

THIS MAN IS UP TO SOMETHING.

WELL, HOW DOES HE MANAGE TO KEEP THEM SO WELL-LAUNDERED?

AH! THE ANSWER IS IN YOUR OWN QUESTION, JAHANPANAH.

HE HAS A TEAM OF EFFICIENT LAUNDERERS.

WELL, THAT COULD EASILY BE ARRANGED.

I'LL SEND FOR THE BEST WASHERMEN IN TOWN. OUR ELEPHANTS TOO MUST LOOK WHITE.

JUST A MINUTE, JAHANPANAH.

I HAVE A NEIGHBOUR WHO IS BY FAR THE BEST WASHERMAN IN TOWN.

OH! SO HE IS OUT TO CORNER HIS NEIGHBOUR.

I'LL SEND FOR HIM AT ONCE.

A LITTLE WHILE LATER —

...AND THE ELEPHANTS SHOULD BE WHITE WITHIN A WEEK.

Y—YES, JAHANPANAH.

AND THE WASHERMAN BEGAN WITH THE FIRST ELEPHANT.

HOWEVER, EVEN AFTER HE SLOGGED AWAY AT THE TASK THE WHOLE DAY LONG, THE ELEPHANT REMAINED AS GREY AS EVER.

THE DOWNCAST WASHERMAN RETRACED HIS STEPS HOMEWARDS.

I'M SURE THIS IS THE POTTER'S DOING.

WHAT IS WRONG, MY GOOD MAN? WHAT WERE YOU BROODING OVER?

SARKAR! YOU HAVE COME AS A GODSEND.

WHEN HE TOLD BIRBAL ALL THAT HAD HAPPENED —

THERE IS A SIMPLE SOLUTION TO THIS PROBLEM. LISTEN...

THE NEXT MORNING —

ISN'T THIS THE SAME ELEPHANT YOU WERE WORKING ON YESTERDAY? WHY! IT HASN'T TURNED EVEN A SHADE WHITER.

I...I HAVE A PROBLEM, JAHANPANAH.

IF I HAD A VESSEL LARGE ENOUGH TO HOLD THE ELEPHANT, I COULD WORK MORE EFFICIENTLY.

RIGHT! WE'LL ORDER A HUGE POT.

I'M GLAD THIS MAN IS GETTING EVEN.

THE POTTER WAS SUMMONED AND THE ORDER PLACED. ONE WEEK LATER —

HA! SO THE WASHERMAN THOUGHT HE COULD OUTWIT ME!

THE POT, JAHANPANAH.

LET THE ELEPHANT ENTER.

THIS IS GOING TO BE FUN.

13

WHAT KIND OF POT HAVE YOU MADE? MAKE ME A NEW ONE AND MAKE SURE IT IS STRONGER! NOW!

BUT... BUT...

GET TO WORK, AT ONCE!

IT WAS ONLY THEN THAT THE POTTER BROKE DOWN AND CONFESSED.

I SUSPECTED THAT HE WAS OUT TO CORNER YOU. BUT WHAT IMPRESSED ME WAS YOUR METHOD OF RETALIATING. YOU DESERVE A REWARD FOR IT.

NO, JAHANPANAH, I DON'T. IT WAS BIRBAL WHO GAVE ME THE IDEA!

I HAD GUESSED THAT TOO. IN FACT I WAS SURE OF IT!

YOU ARE NOT ONLY A JEWEL OF MY COURT BIRBAL, BUT ALSO A TRUE GUARDIAN OF THE INNOCENT.

15

THE CORRUPT OFFICIAL

ONE MORNING IN EMPEROR AKBAR'S COURT —

THIS MAN HAS BEEN FOUND GUILTY OF ACCEPTING BRIBES, JAHANPANAH.

WHAT WAS HE IN CHARGE OF?

THE GRANARIES, JAHANPANAH.

HMM... KEEP HIM IN CUSTODY. WE'LL TRY HIM LATER.

BIRBAL, I HAVE OFTEN WONDERED IF...

DO YOU THINK IT IS A MAN'S OCCUPATION THAT MAKES HIM CORRUPT?

I DON'T THINK SO, JAHANPANAH.

A CORRUPT PERSON, NO MATTER WHAT HIS OCCUPATION, WILL ALWAYS FIND A WAY OF INVITING BRIBES!

I BEG TO DIFFER, JAHANPANAH.

AS USUAL, IT WAS ONE OF BIRBAL'S ADVERSARIES.

I CAN THINK OF A HUNDRED JOBS WHERE THERE'S NO CHANCE FOR A PERSON TO TAKE BRIBES.

CAN YOU NAME JUST ONE!

WHY, YES. HMM...

ASK THE MAN YOU'VE JUST ARRESTED TO SIT ON THE BANKS OF THE JAMUNA AND COUNT THE RIPPLES ON THE WATER.

I'M SURE THIS IS A JOB WHERE BRIBERY IS OUT OF THE QUESTION.

I WOULD BE MOST HAPPY IF A CORRUPT OFFICIAL COULD BE REFORMED. BUT I DON'T THINK EVEN THIS SCHEME WILL HELP.

IT WILL. YOU JUST WATCH.

ACCORDINGLY, THE CORRUPT MAN WAS INSTRUCTED ON HIS NEW DUTIES.

A WEEK LATER —

BIRBAL, THERE ARE NO REPORTS ABOUT OUR CORRUPT OFFICIAL.

WHAT DID I TELL YOU?

WELL...

...I SUGGEST WE GO AND TAKE A LOOK AT HIM?

LET US GO THEN.

WE'LL GO TOMORROW MORNING DISGUISED AS FISHERMEN.

THE NEXT MORNING —

THERE'S OUR MAN.

!

HEY YOU! WHAT DO YOU THINK YOU'RE DOING?

JUST ROWING.

THE ANSWER IS NO

FOR MONTHS TOGETHER SULTAN KHAN HAD BEEN PLANNING TO STRENGTHEN HIS LOBBY IN THE COURT BY TRYING TO GET HIS CLEVER, BUT NOTORIOUSLY CRAFTY SON, A KEY POSITION IN THE ROYAL SERVICES.

AT LAST —

I WILL TAKE HIM WITH ME TO THE DARBAR EVERY DAY AND WAIT FOR THE OPPORTUNITY TO ACT.

THEIR DAILY RITUAL DID NOT ESCAPE BIRBAL'S WATCHFUL EYE.

SO NOW SULTAN KHAN HAS STARTED BRINGING HIS RASCALLY SON TO THE COURT.

I'M SURE HE IS AIMING FOR THAT VACANT POST OF THE TREASURER. HMM...

ONE MORNING, A FEW DAYS LATER —

WHERE IS BIRBAL TODAY?

HE HASN'T ARRIVED YET, JAHAN-PANAH.

WHY IS HE LATE?

THE EMPEROR IS ANNOYED WITH BIRBAL. THIS IS THE GOLDEN MOMENT.

LET'S SNATCH IT.

JAHANPANAH, DON'T YOU THINK BIRBAL IS TAKING THE COURT FOR GRANTED THESE DAYS?

HMM...

THIS LOOKS LIKE YET ANOTHER TRAP FOR BIRBAL.

HOW COULD HE TAKE THE DARBAR TIMINGS FOR GRANTED?

WE SHOULD TEACH HIM A LESSON, SHOULDN'T WE?

EXACTLY, JAHANPANAH.

CAN YOU THINK OF SOMETHING?

YOU COULD POSSIBLY START BY REFUSING EACH ONE OF HIS REQUESTS TODAY.

REFUSE TO AGREE WITH HIM, JAHANPANAH. SAY *NO* TO WHATEVER HE ASKS FOR.

ALL RIGHT! I WILL BEGIN BY SAYING NO TO WHATEVER HE ASKS FOR.

AND LET'S SEE WHAT BIRBAL COMES UP WITH, THIS TIME.

IT'S BEEN A LONG TIME SINCE I PLAYED SUCH A GAME WITH HIM.

A LITTLE WHILE LATER, BIRBAL ARRIVED.

WHY ARE YOU LATE, BIRBAL?

MY WIFE WAS INDISPOSED. I HAD TO...

I DON'T BELIEVE YOU, BIRBAL.

?

SULTAN KHAN MUST HAVE SOMETHING TO DO WITH THIS.

IT'S THE TRUTH. PLEASE ACCEPT MY APOLOGIES, JAHANPANAH.

NO. I REFUSE TO.

SHALL WE GET DOWN TO DISCUSSING MATTERS OF STATE, THEN?

NO! WE WILL NOT.

OH! SO, 'NO' IS THE NAME OF THE GAME. WELL, WELL...

THEN PLEASE PERMIT ME TO LEAVE THE DARBAR AND GO HOME.

NO. I WILL NOT PERMIT YOU.

NOW I'LL GO AND ASK THE EMPEROR TO GIVE YOU THE APPOINTMENT.

JUST AS SULTAN KHAN WAS ABOUT TO SPEAK UP—

HOWEVER, THERE IS ONE REQUEST I MUST MAKE TODAY, JAHANPANAH.

THE WISE ANSWER

LATE ONE EVENING, AS THE EMPEROR WAS ABOUT TO RETIRE TO HIS QUARTERS —

WHAT IS IT, AMIR?

A PANDIT FROM THE SOUTH IS HERE TO SEE YOU AND BIRBAL, JAHANPANAH!

WHAT DOES HE WANT?

HE'S HEARD A LOT ABOUT YOUR WISDOM AND BIRBAL'S WIT.

HE WOULD LIKE TO ASK BIRBAL A FEW QUESTIONS.

AT THIS HOUR?

BUT ONE SHOULDN'T DISAPPOINT A LEARNED PANDIT. SHOW HIM IN, AMIR.

IT'S BEEN A HARD DAY AT COURT, BIRBAL. BE QUICK WITH THIS MAN.

YES, PANDITJI, YOUR QUESTIONS.

O WISE BIRBAL, WOULD YOU LIKE TO ANSWER A HUNDRED EASY QUESTIONS OR JUST A SINGLE DIFFICULT ONE?

THE EMPEROR IS IN NO MOOD TO SIT THROUGH A HUNDRED QUESTIONS.

PLEASE ASK ME A SINGLE DIFFICULT QUESTION, PANDITJI.

ALL RIGHT. WHICH CAME FIRST—THE HEN OR THE EGG?

THE HEN OF COURSE!

HOW CAN YOU BE SO SURE?

THAT, I'M AFRAID, IS YOUR SECOND QUESTION, PANDITJI. WE HAD AGREED THAT I WOULD ANSWER ONLY ONE.

AND THE PANDIT STOOD ADMIRING BIRBAL'S WIT — OF WHICH HE HAD ONLY HEARD BEFORE.

THE WAX PRINCE

BIRBAL, YOUR GODS ARE REALLY FUNNY.

EMPEROR AKBAR RESPECTS MY HINDU RELIGION AS MUCH AS HE REVERES ISLAM. SURELY HE IS TRYING TO TEASE ME.

LOOK AT YOUR KRISHNA. DOESN'T HE HAVE ANY HELPERS OR ASSISTANTS?

WHENEVER HIS DEVOTEES CALL FOR HELP, HE HIMSELF COMES RUNNING TO THEIR AID. SURELY HE COULD SEND SOMEONE ELSE.

WELL, WELL...

THE KING DOTES ON HIS GRANDSON. THAT GIVES ME AN IDEA.

I WANT A WAX MODEL MADE TO LOOK EXACTLY LIKE THE EMPEROR'S GRANDSON.

YES, HUZOOR. I'LL HAVE IT READY.

BIRBAL CALLED THE CHILD'S ATTENDANT ASIDE.

WHY, HUZOOR, THIS STATUE LOOKS EXACTLY LIKE PRINCE KHURRAM.

SO IT DOES. I HAVE DRESSED IT IN HIS CLOTHES AND JEWELS.

NOW I WANT YOU TO CARRY THIS STATUE IN YOUR ARMS AND GO TO THE ROYAL GARDEN.

THEN GO NEAR THE POND AND PRETEND TO TRIP SO THAT THE STATUE SLIPS INTO THE WATER.

AS YOU SAY, HUZOOR.

BIRBAL HURRIED TO BRING AKBAR OUT TO THE GARDEN.

THE SIGHT THAT MET AKBAR'S EYES AS HE ENTERED THE GARDEN, SHOCKED HIM.

OH! WHAT HAVE YOU DONE?

MY DARLING GRANDSON!

THANK GOD! THIS IS ONLY A WAX STATUE.

BUT, YOUR MAJESTY, WHY DID YOU JUMP INTO THE POND YOURSELF? DON'T YOU HAVE SERVANTS TO HELP YOU?

I DO! BUT MY GRANDSON IS SO PRECIOUS. I COULDN'T WAIT TO CALL ANYONE.

PRECISELY, YOUR MAJESTY! TO LORD KRISHNA, HIS DEVOTEES ARE VERY PRECIOUS.

YOU HAVE PROVED YOUR POINT, AS USUAL BIRBAL.

AMAR CHITRA KATHA

BIRBAL THE WISE

THE ADVENTURES OF AKBAR'S FAVOURITE MINISTER

The route to your roots

BIRBAL THE WISE

Every ruler needs a friend like Birbal – faithful, intelligent and blessed with a wonderful sense of humour. Birbal dealt with every tricky situation, every palace intrigue, and every demand of his petulant queen with characteristic aplomb. His gentle tact gave him a unique advantage – he became the all-powerful Akbar's alter ego. With wisdom to match his wit, he soon had both friend and foe under his spell.

Script	Illustrations	Editor
Anant Pai	Ram Waeerkar	Anant Pai

BIRBAL THE WISE

THE WICKED BARBER

BIRBAL WAS A MINISTER AT THE COURT OF EMPEROR AKBAR. BOTH, HINDUS AND MUSLIMS AT THE COURT, LIKED HIM FOR HIS READY WIT AND KEEN SENSE OF HUMOUR. HOWEVER, THERE WERE A FEW WHO ENVIED HIM.

THEY HATCHED A PLOT TO KILL HIM. WITH THIS IN VIEW, THEY MET THE EMPEROR'S BARBER TO ASK FOR HIS HELP.

HAJAM＊ SAHAB, IF YOU WILL DO US A SMALL FAVOUR, WE WILL GIVE YOU A BAG FULL OF GOLD.

WHAT DO YOU WANT ME TO DO?

BUZZ... BUZZ

REST ASSURED, I'LL TELL THE EMPEROR TOMORROW.

THE NEXT MORNING—

JAHANPANAH⊕, I HAVE OFTEN WONDERED...

WHY DO YOU HESITATE? BE FRANK, MY MAN. SPEAK UP!

JAHANPANAH, HAS IT EVER OCCURRED TO YOU THAT YOU ARE DOING NOTHING FOR THE WELFARE OF YOUR ANCESTORS?

＊ BARBER ⊕ REFUGE OF THE WORLD.

BUT THEY ARE DEAD AND IN HEAVEN. HOW AM I TO KNOW WHAT THEY NEED?

YOU CAN SEND SOMEONE THERE TO FIND OUT.

INDEED! IT'S A GOOD IDEA! CAN YOU SUGGEST HOW IT'S TO BE DONE?

A THOUSAND BUNDLES OF HAY SHOULD BE PILED IN THE OPEN GROUND OUTSIDE THE CITY. AFTER A CHOSEN MAN ASCENDS THE PILE, IT MUST BE SET ALIGHT.

AND THE MAN WILL RISE STRAIGHT UP TO HEAVEN ALONG WITH THE SMOKE.

BUT WHO...?

WHO ELSE BUT THE WISE BIRBAL?

SO THAT'S IT! ONE MORE TRAP SET FOR MY TRUST- ED FRIEND. BUT I CAN TRUST HIM TO GET OUT OF IT.

ALL RIGHT. THEN BIRBAL SHALL GO.

THAT EVENING, THE EMPEROR ANNOUNCED HIS PLAN AT COURT.

...AND BIRBAL, I HAVE CHOSEN YOU FOR THE TASK. PLEASE GO TO HEAVEN AND SEE IF MY ANCESTORS NEED ANYTHING.

?

BIRBAL IMMEDIATELY GOT A FEW TRUSTED WORKMEN TO DIG A TUNNEL FROM HIS HOUSE TO THE OPEN GROUND WHERE THE BUNDLES OF HAY WERE BEING PILED UP.

ON THE APPOINTED DAY, EVERYONE GATHERED TO SEE BIRBAL ASCEND TO HEAVEN.

I WOULD LIKE TO LIE DOWN HERE. PLEASE START PILING THE HAY AROUND ME.

BIRBAL HAD CHOSEN A SPOT NEAR THE ENTRANCE TO HIS TUNNEL WHICH HAD BEEN CLEVERLY CONCEALED BY A FEW BUNDLES OF HAY.

WHEN THE BUNDLES OF HAY BEGAN TO BURN, BIRBAL'S FRIENDS SHED TEARS...

POOR MAN! HOW CAN HE COME BACK ALIVE? HE WAS A GOOD AND NOBLE SOUL — A REAL FRIEND INDEED!

...BUT HIS ENEMIES REJOICED.

WE HAVE AT LAST GOT RID OF HIM. WE MUST CELEBRATE THE OCCASION.

MEANWHILE —

ONCE I REACH HOME, I WILL REMAIN THERE FOR A FEW MONTHS TILL I THINK OF A PLAN TO PUNISH THE BARBER.

SIX MONTHS LATER, WHEN BIRBAL ENTERED THE COURT, NO ONE RECOGNISED HIM.

WHO COULD THAT MAN BE? WHAT DOES HE WANT HERE?

AKBAR, HOWEVER, RE-COGNISED HIM IMME-DIATELY.

JUST AS I HAD ANTICIPATED... BIRBAL HAS ESCAPED, UNHURT.

JAHANPANAH, I COME STRAIGHT FROM HEAVEN.

IT IS GOOD TO SEE YOU AGAIN, BIRBAL.

HOW IS EVERY-BODY UP THERE? HOW IS MY FATHER?

THEY ARE ALL FINE AND HAVE ALL THE COMFORTS UP THERE. BUT THERE IS ONE THING THEY LACK— A GOOD BARBER...

...WHICH EXPLAINS MY UNCUT HAIR AND BEARD. YOUR FORE-FATHERS ARE UNHAPPY ABOUT THIS, AND WANT YOU TO SEND THEM A GOOD BARBER.

THAT SHOULD NOT BE DIFFICULT NOW THAT WE KNOW HOW THE JOURNEY CAN BE MADE. BUT WHO...

WHO ELSE BUT THE ROYAL BARBER! YOUR FATHER WAS PARTICULARLY FOND OF HIM.

GOOD. I WILL DO AS YOU SAY.

WHEN THE BARBER RECEIVED THE ORDERS, HE RAN TO THE COURTIERS WHO HAD PLOTTED AGAINST BIRBAL.

PLEASE DO SOMETHING TO SAVE ME, I BEG OF YOU.

WHAT CAN WE DO?

REALISING THAT HE WAS TRAPPED, THE FRIGHTENED BARBER TOOK TO HIS HEELS AND WAS NEVER HEARD OF AGAIN.

BEGUM RECONCILED

HUSSAIN KHAN, AS THE EMPEROR'S BROTHER-IN-LAW, YOU OUGHT TO BE THE MINISTER INSTEAD OF BIRBAL.

BUT THE EMPEROR DOES NOT THINK SO.

THIS TIME, THE PLOTTERS HAD DECIDED TO MAKE USE OF HUSSAIN KHAN, THE EMPEROR'S BROTHER-IN-LAW, TO ACHIEVE THEIR GOAL.

WHY DON'T YOU ASK YOUR SISTER TO PLEAD YOUR CASE WITH THE EMPEROR?

A GOOD IDEA. HOW STRANGE THAT I DIDN'T THINK OF IT EARLIER!

A FEW DAYS LATER —

BEGUM, YOU SEEM TO BE UPSET ABOUT SOMETHING. WON'T YOU CONFIDE IN ME?

I WANT YOU TO MAKE MY BROTHER THE MINISTER AT YOUR COURT, IN BIRBAL'S PLACE.

HOW CAN I DO THAT? IT NEEDS INTELLI- GENCE TO RUN THE AFFAIRS OF SUCH A VAST EMPIRE; AND YOUR BROTHER DOES NOT HAVE ENOUGH OF IT.

BESIDES, HOW CAN I OUST BIRBAL FROM THE POST UNLESS I HAVE A REASON?

GIVE HIM AN IMPOSSIBLE TASK TO PERFORM. HE IS BOUND TO FAIL. AND THEN...

ALL RIGHT. YOU SUGGEST THE TASK.

WHEN YOU ARE IN THE PALACE GARDEN TO- MORROW, INSIST THAT HE BRING ME TO YOU. HE WILL NOT SUCCEED, COME WHAT MAY.

YOU ARE CAUGHT THIS TIME BIRBAL. IT IS IN MY POWER TO SEE YOU FAIL.

THE NEXT DAY—

JAHANPANAH, YOU SEEM TROUBLED. WHAT IS THE MATTER?

IT'S MY BEGUM. SHE IS ANNOYED WITH ME AND REFUSES TO SEE ME.

GO BRING HER TO ME THIS MINUTE. ONLY YOU CAN DO IT.

IF YOU FAIL, YOU WILL LOSE YOUR POST. I WILL APPOINT HUSSAIN KHAN AS MY MINISTER. THAT WOULD PLEASE MY BEGUM.

SO THAT'S THEIR GAME THIS TIME!

BIRBAL WORE AN ABJECT LOOK, AS HE STOOD BEFORE THE BEGUM.

BEGUM SAHIBA, I COME WITH A MESSAGE FROM THE EMPEROR.

HE IS IN THE PALACE GARDEN. HE WANTS YOU TO···

JUST THEN A MESSENGER WALKED UP TO HIM.

WHAT IS IT?

THIS MESSAGE IS ONLY FOR YOUR EARS, HUZUR *

AS THE MESSENGER WHISPERED INTO BIRBAL'S EAR, THREE OF HIS WORDS WERE LOUD AND CLEAR.

BUZZ··· BUZZ···SHE IS BEAUTIFUL···

13

BIRBAL TURNED TO THE BEGUM.

NOW THE WHOLE SITUATION HAS CHANGED. YOU NEED NOT COME, BEGUM SAHIBA.

SOON AFTER, BIRBAL LEFT—

WHAT! DID I NOT OVERHEAR SOMETHING ABOUT A BEAUTIFUL MAIDEN? PERHAPS THE EMPEROR DOES NOT WANT ME TO SEE HIM WITH HER.

BURNING WITH JEALOUS CURIOSITY, THE BEGUM HURRIED TOWARDS THE PALACE GARDEN.

SHE WAS SURPRISED TO SEE THE EMPEROR ALONE.

BEGUM! BUT YOU HAD PROMISED THAT YOU WOULD NOT COME!

THE DEAREST OBJECT

ONE DAY, FOR SOME REASON, AKBAR BECAME DISPLEASED WITH HIS BEGUM.

I ORDER YOU TO LEAVE THE PALACE WITHIN A DAY.

JAHANPANAH, HOW CAN I LIVE WITHOUT YOU? PLEASE DON'T SEND ME AWAY.

I HAVE MADE UP MY MIND. YOU WILL HAVE TO GO. HOWEVER, YOU MAY TAKE WITH YOU THE OBJECTS THAT ARE DEAR TO YOU.

AS THE DEJECTED BEGUM WONDERED WHAT TO DO, A THOUGHT SUDDENLY OCCURRED TO HER.

PERHAPS, BIRBAL CAN HELP ME.

16

SHE SENT FOR BIRBAL AND EXPLAINED THE SITUATION TO HIM.

HE SAID YOU COULD TAKE WHATEVER WAS DEAR TO YOU, DIDN'T HE?

WHEN BIRBAL LEFT AFTER TELLING THE BEGUM WHAT SHE SHOULD DO —

PACK MY BELONGINGS. I AM GOING HOME FOR A FEW DAYS.

WHEN ALL HER BELONGINGS WERE PACKED —

NOW, TELL YOUR MASTER THAT I WOULD LIKE TO SEE HIM BEFORE I LEAVE.

WHEN AKBAR ARRIVED —

MAY I OFFER YOU A GLASS OF SHERBET, PLEASE?

I HAVE NO OBJECTION.

AFTER AKBAR DRANK THE SHERBET —

I FEEL SLEEPY.

LATER —

ARE THE PALANQUINS READY?

THEY ARE, BEGUM SAHIBA.

WITH THE SLEEPING EMPEROR IN ONE PALANQUIN AND THE BEGUM SAHIBA IN THE OTHER, THE PARTY LEFT AGRA...

...AND IN A FEW HOURS REACHED THE BEGUM'S FATHER'S HOUSE.

I AM PLEASED TO SEE YOU, DEAR. BUT WHY HAVE YOU COME AT SUCH AN ODD TIME?

FATHER, I WILL EXPLAIN EVERYTHING LATER. LET US FIRST MAKE ARRANGEMENTS FOR THE EMPEROR'S STAY.

HE IS STILL ASLEEP.

HE WILL WAKE UP IN ANOTHER HOUR OR SO.

AN HOUR LATER —

WHERE AM I?

ISN'T THIS YOUR FATHER'S HOUSE? HOW DID I COME HERE?

JAHANPANAH, YOU HAD ORDERED ME TO LEAVE THE PALACE...

...BUT YOU HAD GIVEN ME PERMISSION TO CARRY AWAY ANYTHING THAT WAS DEAR TO ME. NOTHING IS MORE DEAR TO ME THAN YOU. SO, I BROUGHT YOU AWAY WITH ME.

WHAT?

HOW DARE SHE MAKE A FOOL OF ME!

BUT IT WAS BRILLIANTLY DONE!

HA! HA! THAT WAS A CLEVER MOVE, INDEED. HA! HA! HA!

I AM PLEASED WITH YOU. LET US GO BACK. BUT TELL ME, WHOSE IDEA WAS IT?

WHO BUT BIRBAL COULD HAVE THOUGHT OF IT?

AFTER THIS INCIDENT, THE BEGUM FELT EVER OBLIGED TO BIRBAL FOR RE-STORING HER TO HER HUSBAND'S FAVOUR.

BIRBAL'S VISIT TO BURMA

HUSSAIN KHAN COULD NOT GIVE UP THE IDEA THAT HE OUGHT TO BE THE MINISTER AND NOT BIRBAL. SINCE HE COULD NOT INDUCE HIS SISTER TO SPEAK FOR HIM, HE ASKED THE COURTIERS TO SPEAK TO THE EMPEROR.

THEY WERE ONLY TOO GLAD TO DO SO.

JAHANPANAH! WE HAVE HAD A HINDU MINISTER FOR A LONG TIME. IS IT NOT FAIR TO GIVE HUSSAIN KHAN A CHANCE, NOW?

AKBAR THOUGHT FOR A WHILE.

IT SEEMS THESE PEOPLE ARE BENT ON MAKING HUSSAIN KHAN MY MINISTER. I MUST SETTLE THIS MATTER ONCE AND FOR ALL.

A FEW DAYS LATER —

THIS IS A SEALED LETTER, TO THE KING OF BURMA.

SINCE IT IS EXTREMELY IMPORTANT, I WANT BIRBAL AND HUSSAIN KHAN TO GO TO BURMA AND DELIVER IT PERSONALLY.

BIRBAL AND HUSSAIN KHAN SET OUT ON THE JOURNEY.

AT BURMA —

WE SEEK AN AUDIENCE WITH THE KING. WE HAVE AN URGENT MESSAGE FOR HIM FROM THE EMPEROR OF HINDUSTAN.*

* INDIA

THE KING WAS SURPRISED WHEN THE GUARD ANNOUNCED THE MESSAGE.

DOES THE EMPEROR HAVE EVIL DESIGNS ON BURMA?

SEND THEM IN.

BUT WHEN HE READ THE LETTER —

HOW CAN THIS BE? WHAT DOES IT MEAN?

HE TURNED TO HIS MINISTER —

MAKE ARRANGE-MENTS FOR THEIR STAY. KEEP A CLOSE WATCH ON THEM. SEE TO IT THAT THEY DON'T ESCAPE.

LATER, WHEN THEY WERE ALONE, THE KING CONFIDED IN HIS MINISTER.

THE EMPEROR OF HINDUSTAN WANTS ME TO HANG THESE TWO MEN ON THE NIGHT OF THE FULL MOON. WHAT DOES THAT MEAN?

THERE IS SOMETHING SUSPICIOUS IN IT. WHY COULDN'T HE HANG THEM IN AGRA?

PERHAPS THEY ARE POWERFUL MEN AT HIS COURT. AND HE DID NOT WANT ANYONE TO KNOW THAT THE EMPEROR HAD CAUSED THEM HARM.

IF THESE MEN DO HAVE BACKING AT THE COURT, THEN THOSE WHO WILL COME TO POWER AFTER AKBAR WILL BE ANGRY WITH US FOR KILLING THEIR LEADERS. WE MUST FIND OUT MORE ABOUT THEM.

JUST THEN, THE DOOR OF THEIR ROOM OPENED AND IN CAME THE MINISTER.

HE CAME TO BIRBAL.

I UNDERSTAND, ONE OF YOU IS BIRBAL AND THE OTHER HUSSAIN KHAN. EMPEROR AKBAR HAS REQUESTED THAT BOTH OF YOU BE HANGED ON THE NIGHT OF THE FULL MOON. WHY?

OUR EMPEROR IS KIND AND JUST. PLEASE CARRY OUT HIS ORDERS.

HUSSAIN KHAN TURNED PALE WITH FEAR. BUT HE DID NOT FORGET TO TAKE THE CUE FROM BIRBAL.

YES, YOU MUST HANG US ON THE NIGHT OF THE FULL MOON.

THE BAFFLED MINISTER REPORTED THE MATTER TO HIS KING.

YOUR MAJESTY, I THINK THERE MUST BE SOME REASON WHY THESE MEN WANT TO BE HANGED ON THE NIGHT OF THE FULL MOON.

IF WE DON'T CARRY OUT THE ORDER, THE EMPEROR OF HINDUSTAN WILL BE ANGRY.

MEANWHILE, BIRBAL DISCUSSED HIS PLANS WITH HUSSAIN KHAN.

...WHEN THEY TAKE US TO THE GALLOWS, I WILL INSIST THAT I BE HANGED FIRST. YOU MUST DO THE SAME.

ON THE NIGHT OF THE FULL MOON—

YOUR MAJESTY! IT WAS I WHO HAD HANDED OVER THE EMPEROR'S LETTER TO YOU. KINDLY HANG ME FIRST.

I AM THE EMPEROR'S BROTHER-IN-LAW. I BEG OF YOU TO HANG ME FIRST.

THE MINISTER TURNED TO BIRBAL.

IF YOU TELL US WHY YOU ARE SO ANXIOUS TO BE HANGED, WE WILL HANG YOU FIRST.

IS THAT A PROMISE?

YES.

IT IS DESTINED THAT THE ONE WHO IS KILLED HERE TODAY WILL BECOME THE KING OF THIS COUNTRY, IN HIS NEXT BIRTH.

THE KING HAD HURRIED CONSULTATIONS WITH HIS MINISTERS.

I CERTAINLY DO NOT WANT ANYONE EXCEPT MY SON TO BE THE KING OF THIS COUNTRY.

I SUGGEST WE WRITE TO THE EMPEROR THAT SINCE HE HAS NOT GIVEN ANY INDICATION OF THE NATURE OF THE CRIME COMMITTED BY THESE MEN, WE CANNOT HANG THEM.

WHEN THE DECISION WAS ANNOUNCED—

YOUR MAJESTY! IT IS VERY UNFAIR ON THE PART OF THE MINISTER TO GO BACK ON HIS PROMISE.

LET A CLOSE WATCH BE KEPT ON THESE MEN TO ENSURE THAT THEY DO NOT GET KILLED OR THAT THEY DO NOT COMMIT SUICIDE.

JUST AS BIRBAL HAD EXPECTED, THEY WERE ESCORTED TO THE BORDER OF AKBAR'S EMPIRE.

WHEN THE TWO REACHED EMPEROR AKBAR'S COURT—

DID YOU ENJOY THE TRIP TO BURMA?

YES, JAHANPANAH! WE WERE TREATED WITH GREAT HONOUR AND ESCORTED BACK.

LATER, WHEN HUSSAIN KHAN TOLD AKBAR ALL THAT HAD HAPPENED IN BURMA—

WOULD YOU LIKE TO BE MY MINISTER, HUSSAIN KHAN?

NO, JAHANPANAH. THAT POST CAN ONLY BELONG TO BIRBAL. HIS WISDOM IS UNMATCHED.

SEVEN KANDS!
One Legendary Tale!

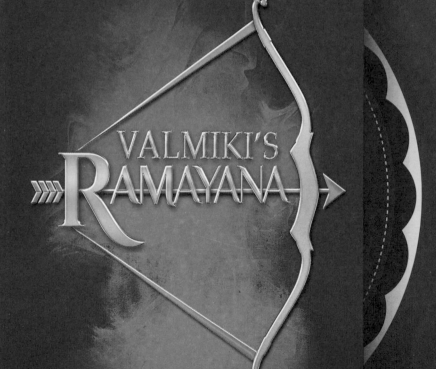

VALMIKI'S RAMAYANA

TAKE AN EPIC JOURNEY
FROM AYODHYA TO LANKA AND BACK!

BUY NOW ON www.amarchitrakatha.com

BIRBAL TO
THE RESCUE
THE MASTER PSYCHOLOGIST

The route to your roots

BIRBAL TO
THE RESCUE

Pity the thief or hypocrite who crosses Birbal's path. The poor man will be either hopelessly embarrassed or pleased to escape with his life. With an unfailing eye for himan weakness, Birbal protects the innocent. People, from every strata of society, flock to him for help with endless lists of woes. Known for his compassion and tact, Birbal never fails them, even if it means pitting his wits against the all-powerful Emperor.

Script
Meera Ugra

Illustrations
Ram Waeerkar

Editor
Anant Pai

A POTFUL OF WISDOM

ONE DAY, AN ENVOY FROM THE COURT OF THE KING OF CEYLON CAME TO AKBAR'S COURT ON A STRANGE MISSION.

JAHANPANAH, YOU HAVE MANY WISE MEN AT YOUR COURT. I HAVE BEEN SENT BY MY KING TO REQUEST YOU FOR A POTFUL OF WISDOM.

A POTFUL OF WISDOM? WHAT A RIDICULOUS REQUEST!

THE KING OF CEYLON IS OUT TO BAFFLE US.

AND HE'LL SUCCEED. NO ONE, NOT EVEN BIRBAL, CAN GET US OUT OF THIS ONE.

1

WELL, BIRBAL?

JAHANPANAH, WE COULD EASILY SPARE SOME WISDOM.

BUT IT'LL TAKE TIME — PERHAPS A FEW WEEKS.

I'M WILLING TO WAIT.

LATER —

WELL, BIRBAL. I HOPE YOU KNOW WHAT YOU'RE DOING. OUR PRESTIGE IS AT STAKE.

DON'T WORRY, JAHANPANAH. THE KING OF CEYLON SHALL HAVE HIS POTFUL OF WISDOM.

THAT EVENING, BIRBAL SENT FOR HIS ATTENDANT.

BRING ME A FEW CLAY POTS WITH NARROW NECKS.

THE ATTENDANT SOON CAME BACK WITH THE POTS.

AH! THERE YOU ARE! GOOD. FOLLOW ME TO THE PUMPKIN PATCH.

AT THE PUMPKIN PATCH —

GIVE ME ONE OF THOSE POTS.

BIRBAL CAREFULLY PLACED THE POT OVER A PUMPKIN FLOWER.

NOW PLACE THE OTHER POTS IN THE SAME MANNER.

WHEN THE ATTENDANT FINISHED PLACING THE LAST POT —

KEEP AN EYE ON THESE, AND DON'T LET THEM BE MOVED.

I'LL HAVE THEM COLLECTED LATER.

ANY TIME, HUZUR.

3

A FEW WEEKS LATER —

HAVE YOU MADE ANY PROGRESS, BIRBAL?

YES, JAHANPANAH. I'M ALMOST THROUGH WITH THE TASK.

I SHOULD BE ABLE TO HAVE THE POT FILLED IN... SAY... A FORTNIGHT.

A FORTNIGHT LATER —

AHA — NOW THEY ARE ALMOST AS BIG AS THE POTS! GOOD!

YOU SHALL BE HANDSOMELY REWARDED FOR YOUR LABOUR.

LATER BIRBAL HAD THE ENVOY SUMMONED TO COURT.

THE POTFUL OF WISDOM IS READY, JAHANPANAH.

BIRBAL CLAPPED HIS HANDS —

THE NEXT MOMENT, HIS ATTENDANT WALKED SOLEMNLY IN, CARRYING A TRAY WITH A POT ON IT.

HERE YOU ARE. YOU MAY TAKE IT TO YOUR KING. BUT REMEMBER...

...OUR PRECIOUS POT MUST BE RETURNED EMPTY AND INTACT. AND...

...THE FRUIT OF WISDOM THAT IT CONTAINS, TO BE OF ANY VALUE, MUST BE REMOVED WITHOUT A SCRATCH!

AS SOON AS THE ENVOY LEFT —

BIRBAL, I AM CURIOUS TO HAVE A LOOK AT THE FRUIT OF WISDOM. YOU SAID YOU HAVE FIVE MORE.

I'LL HAVE THEM SENT TO YOU, JAHAN-PANAH.

WHEN THE OTHER POTS WERE BROUGHT, AKBAR LOOKED INTO ONE OF THEM...

?

HA! HA! HA! THE FRUIT OF WISDOM INDEED! IT WILL CERTAINLY MAKE THE KING OF CEYLON A WISER MAN, THOUGH!

THE EMPEROR'S TOUCH

ONE DAY, AN OLD WOMAN AND HER WIDOWED DAUGHTER-IN-LAW CAME TO BIRBAL.

MY SON HAD SERVED IN THE ROYAL ARMY FOR TWENTY YEARS. BUT NOW, HE IS DEAD AND WE HAVE NO ONE TO TURN TO!

OUR EMPEROR IS KIND AND GENEROUS. HE WILL HELP YOU. DO AS I SAY.

THE FOLLOWING DAY, AT COURT—

JAHANPANAH, THIS SWORD ONCE WIELDED BY MY SON HAS WON MANY BATTLES FOR YOU. SO, PLEASE KEEP IT IN THE ARMOURY.

LET ME SEE IT.

THE SWORD WAS HANDED OVER TO THE EMPEROR. HE EXAMINED IT CAREFULLY.

IT'S OLD AND RUSTY... OF NO USE TO US WHATSOEVER.

HE GAVE THE SWORD TO AN ATTENDANT.

RETURN IT TO HER AND GIVE HER FIVE GOLD COINS FOR HER TROUBLE.

JUST FIVE GOLD COINS!

MAY I INSPECT THE SWORD, JAHANPANAH?

BIRBAL TOOK THE SWORD...

...AND LOOKED AT IT CLOSELY...

...AGAIN AND AGAIN.

?

WHY, BIRBAL, WHAT'S WRONG?

NOTHING, JAHAN-PANAH. IT'S ONLY THAT... I WAS CONFIDENT THE SWORD WOULD HAVE TURNED GOLDEN.

TURNED GOLDEN?

YES, JAHANPANAH. WHEN EVEN THE PARAS *, A MERE STONE, CAN TRANSMUTE IRON INTO GOLD...

...I'M SURPRISED THAT WHILE PASSING THROUGH YOUR BENEVOLENT HANDS...

...WELL...

AKBAR UNDERSTOOD.

GIVE THE WOMAN GOLD EQUAL TO THE WEIGHT OF THE SWORD.

AFTER RECEIVING THE GOLD, THE WOMEN WENT AWAY BLESSING THE EMPEROR —AND BIRBAL!

* A LEGENDARY STONE CREDITED WITH THE POWER OF CHANGING IRON INTO GOLD

A WIDOW'S SAVINGS

THE RICH AND THE POOR, THE YOUNG AND THE OLD, ALL SOUGHT BIRBAL'S HELP WHEN THEY WERE WRONGED. ONE DAY AN OLD WIDOW CAME TO SEE HIM.

HELP ME, HUZUR. I'VE BEEN SWINDLED.

BY WHOM?

IT'S A LONG STORY, HUZUR. SIX MONTHS AGO, I DECIDED TO GO ON A PILGRIMAGE.

BUT I WAS WORRIED ABOUT MY MONEY. I DIDN'T KNOW WHERE TO KEEP IT.

"FINALLY, I WENT TO A MENDICANT."

HERE IS A BAG OF COPPER COINS — ALL THAT I HAVE IN THIS WORLD. PLEASE KEEP IT FOR ME. IT WILL BE SAFE WITH YOU!

BUT SIR, I DID BURY IT HERE... THREE MONTHS AGO ... IN *YOUR* PRESENCE!

QUITE POSSIBLE. BUT I AM BLIND TO WHAT GOES ON IN THIS MATERIALISTIC WORLD.

MY MIND HAS ONLY ONE THOUGHT—RAMA; MY EARS HEAR ONLY ONE SOUND—RAMA; MY EYES BEHOLD BUT ONE FORM— RAMA!

I CAME AWAY. WHAT ELSE COULD I DO?

COULD THE MENDICANT HAVE STOLEN YOUR COINS?

I AM SURE HE HAS. BUT I HAVE NO PROOF.

HM.

14

15

BIRBAL WENT INTO THE HUT AND FELL PROSTRATE IN FRONT OF THE MENDICANT.

BLESS ME, MASTER.

MAY YOU LIVE LONG, MY CHILD.

I HAVE HEARD PEOPLE TALK ABOUT YOUR SPIRITUAL EMINENCE. TODAY I HAVE HAD THE GOOD FORTUNE OF RECEIVING YOUR BLESSINGS.

I WONDER WHAT HE HAS IN THE CASKET. GOLD? JEWELS?

HOLY ONE, I HATE TO TROUBLE YOU WITH THE PROBLEMS WE FOOLISH MORTALS HAVE. BUT...

SPEAK UP, CHILD. LET ME HELP YOU IF I CAN.

NO, SIR. YOU MUSTN'T. YOU ARE A MAN OF GOD. I SHOULDN'T BURDEN YOU WITH WORLDLY WORRIES.

WHAT! IS HE GOING AWAY WITH THE CASKET?

BUT... BUT WHO ELSE CAN I TRUST IN THIS WICKED, WICKED WORLD? PLEASE GUIDE ME.

HE IS WAVERING. I MUST LAY HANDS ON THAT CASKET.

MY CHILD, CONFIDE IN ME. UN-BURDEN YOURSELF. I WILL HELP YOU. IT IS MY DUTY TO DO SO.

O HOLY ONE, I HAVE TO LEAVE FOR AJMER TO MEET MY BROTHER...

MAY I LEAVE THESE PRECIOUS JEWELS IN YOUR CARE?

PRECIOUS JEWELS! JUST AS I THOUGHT!

CHILD, THE THOUGHT OF WEALTH IS REPULSIVE TO ME. BUT... BUT...

...I'VE PROMISED TO HELP YOU. AND A MAN OF GOD CANNOT GO BACK ON HIS WORD. SINCE I DO NOT TOUCH WEALTH...

...YOU MAY BURY YOUR CASKET IN A CORNER HERE. IT WILL BE ABSOLUTELY SAFE.

HOW KIND YOU ARE!

I SHALL ALWAYS BE GRATEFUL TO YOU.

AH! THAT'S MY CUE.

AS THE OLD WOMAN ENTERED THE HUT —

WHY DID THIS WRETCH HAVE TO COME HERE NOW? WHAT IF SHE STARTS SHOUTING FOR HER MONEY?

SHOULD I LOSE THOSE PRECIOUS JEWELS FOR THE SAKE OF A BAG OF COPPER COINS? NO!

THANK GOD YOU'RE BACK! I'VE BEEN THINKING ABOUT YOUR BAG OF COINS. I'M SURE YOU MADE A MISTAKE THE OTHER DAY!

BUT...

SO CHILD, BURY YOUR CASKET ANYWHERE BUT DO REMEMBER THE PLACE. I DON'T UNDERSTAND ANYTHING ABOUT THESE WORLDLY MATTERS.

I CAN SEE THAT!

JUST THEN AN ATTENDANT CAME TO BIRBAL.

HUZUR, YOUR BROTHER HAS COME TO VISIT YOU! HE WANTS TO MEET YOU IMMEDIATELY.

OH, OH! SO I DON'T HAVE TO GO TO AJMER AFTER ALL!

MAY I THANK YOU FOR YOUR KINDNESS, HOLY ONE?

AND BIRBAL WALKED OUT WITH THE CASKET.

20

THE PERFECT PORTRAIT

ONE DAY, BIRBAL WAS SURPRISED TO FIND THE NORMALLY CHEERFUL COURT ARTIST LOOKING GLUM.

WHAT'S THE MATTER, MY FRIEND?

MY REPUTATION IS AT STAKE.

BUT YOU ARE THE BEST ARTIST THE COURT HAS EVER KNOWN. I DON'T UNDERSTAND...

YOU WILL, WHEN I'VE TOLD YOU THE WHOLE STORY.

THE ARTIST TOOK BIRBAL TO HIS HOUSE AND SHOWED HIM FIVE PORTRAITS.

THEY ARE OF A RICH NOBLE.

AREN'T THESE OF THE SAME MAN?

"A MONTH AGO HE THREW ME A CHALLENGE."

I BET, YOU CAN'T CREATE AN EXACT LIKENESS OF ME.

I BET, I CAN.

"HE POSED AND I GOT DOWN TO WORK. AT LAST —"

THAT'S ALL. I'LL GIVE THE PORTRAIT A FEW FINISHING TOUCHES AND BRING IT TO YOU TOMORROW.

"ON THE FOLLOWING DAY, WHEN I HANDED THE PORTRAIT TO HIM, CONFIDENT OF WINNING THE BET —"

THIS WON'T DO! IT ISN'T AN EXACT LIKENESS. I DON'T HAVE A BEARD!

BUT YOU DID HAVE ONE WHEN YOU POSED FOR THE PORTRAIT!

A BET IS A BET! AND AN EXACT LIKENESS AN EXACT LIKENESS! HERE! YOU MAY KEEP THIS AS A MEMENTO.

PLEASE GIVE ME ANOTHER CHANCE.

ALL RIGHT. YOU MAY TRY AGAIN.

CALM YOURSELF, MY FRIEND. ALL IS NOT LOST! DO AS I TELL YOU AND YOU'LL HAVE THE LAST LAUGH!

A FEW DAYS LATER —

OH, IT'S YOU AGAIN! WHAT HAVE YOU COME WITH NOW? ANOTHER USELESS PORTRAIT?

WHEN THE NOBLE UNWRAPPED THE PARCEL —

A MIRROR!

HOW DARE YOU PLAY GAMES WITH ME! THIS IS NO PORTRAIT! IT'S...

AN EXACT LIKENESS OF YOURSELF! ISN'T THAT WHAT YOU WANTED, MY FRIEND?

THE NOBLE SHEEPISHLY ACCEPTED DEFEAT AND THE ARTIST BECAME HIS CHEERFUL SELF AGAIN.

SPEAK THE TRUTH BUT MAKE IT PLEASANT

THERE HE IS! AT IT AGAIN!

IF BIRBAL'S NEIGHBOUR HAD A WEAKNESS, IT WAS TO HAVE HIS FORTUNE TOLD.

SUDDENLY —

YOU FRAUD! DON'T YOU DARE COME THIS WAY AGAIN!

I WON'T! EVER!

BIRBAL WENT UP TO THE MAN.

WHAT DID YOU DO TO MAKE HIM SO ANGRY?

I READ HIS HOROSCOPE AND PREDICTED THAT HIS NEAR AND DEAR ONES WOULD DIE BEFORE HIM. AND THEN...

HE THREW YOU OUT, DIDN'T HE?

HE DID. HE COULDN'T FACE THE TRUTH, AND...

...I COULDN'T LIE.

YOU DID WELL TO SPEAK THE TRUTH BUT...

...YOU COULD HAVE MADE IT MORE PLEASANT!

PLEASANT? I DON'T UNDERSTAND. HOW...

IT'S SIMPLE. I'LL TELL YOU HOW. LISTEN...

...NOW DO AS I'VE TOLD YOU, AND SEE HOW HE RESPONDS. DON'T FORGET THE DISGUISE!

THE NEXT DAY —

AH, SIR! WHAT A STRIKING PERSONALITY YOU HAVE! MAY I READ YOUR PALM?

CERTAINLY, CERTAINLY, GOOD SIR!

WHAT A GLORIOUS FUTURE! AND WHAT A LONG LIFE! IN FACT...

...YOU'LL LIVE LONGER THAN ALL YOUR NEAR AND DEAR ONES!

REALLY? AND THAT RASCAL SAID YESTERDAY THAT...

NEVER MIND! WHY TALK OF INAUSPICIOUS MATTERS AT THIS AUSPICIOUS MOMENT? WAIT. I HAVE SOMETHING FOR YOU.

HE WENT IN AND CAME OUT WITH A BAG OF COINS.

DO COME AGAIN WHENEVER YOU HAVE THE TIME.

I WILL. MOST CERTAINLY!

LATER —

I NEVER DREAMT, HUZUR, THAT THE MANNER IN WHICH I WORD MY READING IS EVEN MORE IMPORTANT THAN THE READING ITSELF!

THE HOLY PARROT

ONE DAY, AKBAR'S FAVOURITE ATTENDANT CAME TO BIRBAL. HE WAS ALMOST IN TEARS.

HUZUR! HUZUR! YOU'VE GOT TO HELP ME! ONLY YOU CAN SAVE MY LIFE. I... THE EMPEROR...

YES... GO ON...

"A FEW MONTHS AGO, THE EMPEROR GAVE ME A PARROT."

IT'S A VERY SPECIAL BIRD; A HOLY MAN'S GIFT TO ME. TAKE GOOD CARE OF IT.

SHOULD ANYONE BRING ME NEWS OF ITS DEATH, I'LL BEHEAD HIM!

AND NOW... AND NOW IN SPITE OF MY LOVING CARE, IT SUDDENLY DIED. WHAT SHALL I DO?

IS THAT ALL? LEAVE IT TO ME. I'LL TAKE THE NEWS TO THE EMPEROR, AND YET SAVE MY HEAD!

LATER, AT AKBAR'S COURT —

JAHANPANAH, DO YOU REMEMBER THE PARROT THAT FAKIR GAVE YOU? IT'S A HOLY BIRD INDEED!

A HOLY BIRD, INDEED. HA! HA! HA!

IT IS, JAHANPANAH. I HAD GONE TO SEE IT. AND WHAT DO YOU THINK IT WAS DOING?

MEDITATING! WITH ITS EYES CLOSED AND ITS HEAD TURNED SKY-WARDS!

YOU MUST BE JOKING.

SO THE TWO WENT TO THE ATTENDANT'S HOUSE. WHEN AKBAR SAW THE BIRD —

BIRBAL YOU MAY BE WISE, AND CLEVER! BUT THERE IS A LIMIT.

THIS BIRD IS DEAD! AND DON'T TELL ME YOU DIDN'T KNOW IT.

I DID. BUT I DIDN'T WANT TO BE BEHEADED!

ONLY THEN DID AKBAR REMEMBER WHAT HE HAD TOLD HIS ATTENDANT.

WELL! WELL! WELL! YOU'VE SAVED YET ANOTHER HEAD, BIRBAL. AND I'M GRATEFUL TO YOU FOR IT.

AKBAR THE HUNTER

AKBAR WAS EXTREMELY FOND OF HUNTING. ONE DAY—

HELP US, HUZOOR!

OUR VILLAGE IS BEING RAZED!

WHY ON EARTH?

THE KING WANTS MORE FORESTS IN HIS KINGDOM.

HIS MEN HAVE ORDERS TO CREATE MORE AND MORE NEW FORESTS

THE KING WANTS NEW JUNGLES TO HUNT IN.

I'LL TRY AND DO WHAT I CAN.

ON THE NEXT HUNTING TRIP—

AH! THIS IS SO EXHILARATING. DON'T YOU THINK SO, BIRBAL?

UH, HUH!

LOOK AT THOSE OWLS!

CHI-CHI-THUP-THUP

THE TWO GROUPS SEEM TO BE HAVING A QUARREL.

BIRBAL IS SO WISE. HE SHOULD BE ABLE TO MAKE OUT WHAT THEY ARE SAYING

YES, BIRBAL. TELL US WHY THEY ARE FIGHTING

I COULD TELL YOU BUT...

WHY DO YOU HESITATE?

YOUR MAJESTY MAY NOT LIKE TO HEAR IT

GO ON WHY SHOULD I MIND WHAT THE BIRDS SAY?

A GROUP OF OWLS HAVE COME FROM THE NEIGHBOURING KINGDOM TO MARRY ONE OF THEIR BOYS TO A GIRL OWL HERE.

THEY ARE ARRANGING FOR THE MARRIAGE. BUT THERE IS A DISPUTE BETWEEN THE GROOM'S FATHER AND THE BRIDE'S FATHER.

WHY?

THE BOY'S FATHER IS DEMANDING A GIFT OF FORTY FORESTS. BUT THE GIRL'S FATHER IS SAYING HE CANNOT COMPLY NOW...

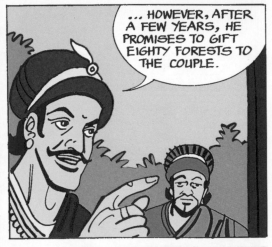

... HOWEVER, AFTER A FEW YEARS, HE PROMISES TO GIFT EIGHTY FORESTS TO THE COUPLE.

HOW? IF HE DOESN'T HAVE FORTY FORESTS NOW, HOW WILL HE GIVE DOUBLE THE NUMBER LATER?

WELL, HE SAYS THE EMPEROR HERE IS VERY FOND OF HUNTING.

HE KEEPS CONVERTING VILLAGES INTO JUNGLES FOR HIS HUNTING PLEASURE SO THE NUMBER OF FORESTS IS SURE TO DOUBLE IN THE FUTURE.

AKBAR UNDERSTOOD THE MESSAGE BIRBAL WAS TRYING TO CONVEY.

YOU ARE RIGHT, BIRBAL. IT IS SELFISH OF ME TO DESTROY VILLAGE AFTER VILLAGE FOR MY HUNTING PLEASURE.

AMAR CHITRA KATHA

THE INIMITABLE BIRBAL

A FRIEND, PHILOSOPHER AND GUIDE TO AKBAR

The route to your roots

THE INIMITABLE BIRBAL

Only Birbal could outwit Akbar and get away with it. A witty and wise diplomat, he ensured that both the emperor and the empire retained their greatness. This collection of tales highlighting Birbal's presence of mind, his kindness and his shrewdness guarantees a good laugh. At the same time, it divulges some useful tricks for overcoming sticky situations.

Script	Illustrations	Editor
Margie Sastry	Ram Waeerkar	Anant Pai

PANDIT GANGARAM

BIRBAL HAD GAINED THE REPUTATION OF BEING A SKILFUL SOLVER OF PROBLEMS. ONE DAY, A BRAHMIN CALLED GANGARAM CAME TO HIM.

BIRBAL SAHIB, I HAVE A PROBLEM WHICH ONLY YOU CAN SOLVE.

WHAT IS IT?

I AM A BRAHMIN BY BIRTH. MY FOREFATHERS WERE GREAT SANSKRIT SCHOLARS. EVERYONE CALLED THEM PANDITS.

YES, I REMEMBER YOUR FATHER.

I HAVE NEITHER MUCH LEARNING NOR WEALTH.

DO YOU WANT ME TO HELP YOU GET WORK?

NO, I AM CONTENTED WITH MY LIFE. BUT I HAVE JUST ONE WISH. I WANT PEOPLE TO ADDRESS ME AS PANDIT.

IS THAT ALL? YOU ONLY WANT TO BE CALLED PANDIT?

YES. I KNOW IT IS DIFFICULT. BUT NO TASK IS DIFFICULT FOR YOU.

I CAN DO IT IN JUST TWO DAYS.

YOU MEAN EVERYONE WILL BEGIN TO CALL ME PANDIT IN JUST TWO DAYS?

WELL, MAYBE THREE. BUT YOU MUST FOLLOW MY INSTRUCTIONS.

I'LL DO ANYTHING YOU SAY.

FOR THE NEXT TWO DAYS, WHENEVER ANYONE CALLS YOU PANDIT, SHOUT AND YELL AT HIM ANGRILY.

WHY SHOULD I DO THAT? I LIKE BEING CALLED PANDIT

DON'T ARGUE. DO AS I SAY.

YES, BIRBAL SAHIB.

WHERE DO YOU LIVE?

BARA CHOWK, SECOND LANE. FOURTH HOUSE.

NEXT DAY BIRBAL WENT TO THAT ADDRESS. HE FOUND SOME SMALL BOYS PLAYING OUTSIDE. HE CALLED ONE ASIDE—

DO YOU KNOW GANGARAM WHO LIVES IN THAT HOUSE?

YES. HE SCOLDED US YESTERDAY BECAUSE WE WERE MAKING A LOT OF NOISE.

I'LL TELL YOU HOW TO GET EVEN. JUST CALL HIM 'PANDITJI'.

SURE ENOUGH, AS SOON AS THE BRAHMIN STEPPED OUT—

PANDITJI

REMEMBERING BIRBAL'S WORDS, GANGARAM POUNCED ON THE BOY.

YOU... HOW DARE YOU CALL ME THAT.

NOW THE OTHER BOYS TOOK UP THE CUE.

PANDITJI!

OHH PANDITJI!

EACH TIME THEY SHOUTED, GANGARAM WOULD CHASE THEM, BRANDISHING HIS STICK.

WAIT TILL I CATCH YOU!

IT BECAME A POPULAR PASTIME IN BARA CHOWK.

YOU WANT TO HAVE SOME FUN? JUST CALL THAT MAN 'PANDITJI'?

SOON, HOWEVER, THEY TIRED OF THE GAME BECAUSE GANGARAM STOPPED ABUSING THEM.

THE GAME STOPPED, BUT THE NAME STUCK.

I HAVE TO GIVE THESE SWEETS TO GANGARAM IN THIS STREET. WHICH IS HIS HOUSE?

DON'T YOU KNOW PANDITJI'S HOUSE? HERE IT IS!

AND CURRY OF COURSE

ONE DAY AKBAR CALLED FOR BIRBAL.

BIRBAL, YOU HAD BEEN TO A WEDDING YESTERDAY.

WHAT DID YOU EAT, BIRBAL?

OH! I HAD LADDUS, PHIRNI, PULAO, HMM...

WHAT ELSE?

LET ME TRY TO REMEMBER. YES, THERE WAS KHEER AS WELL AS BIRYANI.

WHAT ELSE, BIRBAL?

OH, THERE WERE SO MANY THINGS LIKE...

JUST THEN, A COURTIER INTERRUPTED WITH AN IMPORTANT MESSAGE FOR THE EMPEROR, AND THE CONVERSATION REMAINED UNFINISHED. NEXT DAY IN THE DURBAR, AKBAR WANTED TO TEST BIRBAL'S MEMORY. HE TURNED TO HIM —

WHAT ELSE, BIRBAL?

BIRBAL REALISED THAT AKBAR WAS REFERRING TO THE CONVERSATION OF THE PREVIOUS DAY. PROMPTLY HE SAID —

AND CURRY, OF COURSE.

AKBAR WAS IMMENSELY PLEASED.

WAH! BIRBAL. YOU ARE INDEED GREAT. HERE! TAKE THIS PEARL NECKLACE.

THE COURTIERS PRESENT WERE PERPLEXED.

WHY, THE KING MUST REALLY BE FOND OF CURRY. HE GAVE BIRBAL A PRESENT JUST FOR MENTIONING THE WORD CURRY.

AFTER THE COURT HAD DISPERSED, THEY GOT TOGETHER FOR DISCUSSIONS.

WE MUST BRING THE BEST CURRY FOR THE EMPEROR TOMORROW.

YES, LOTS OF IT.

SURELY HE WILL REWARD US TOO

THE NEXT DAY THEY ARRIVED IN THE DURBAR WITH THEIR SERVANTS CARRYING HUGE URNS OF CURRY ON THEIR HEADS.

WHAT'S ALL THIS? WHAT ARE THESE MEN CARRYING TO THE COURT?

WE HAVE BROUGHT CURRY FOR YOU, JAHANPANAH. WE KNOW NOW HOW MUCH YOU LIKE IT.

AKBAR UNDERSTOOD AT ONCE—

YOU FOOLS! WHAT BIRBAL SAID YESTERDAY WAS IN ANOTHER CONTEXT. AS A PUNISHMENT FOR YOUR STUPIDITY I WILL MAKE YOU EAT ALL THIS CURRY JUST NOW.

FORGIVE US! WE WILL NOT ACT IN HASTE NEXT TIME.

BIRBAL HAD A GOOD LAUGH.

THE ONLY ROOSTER

AKBAR LOVED TO PLAY HARMLESS TRICKS ON BIRBAL—

SO MANY TIMES HAVE I TRIED TO TRAP HIM, BUT HE ALWAYS GETS THE BETTER OF ME.

THIS TIME I WILL GET EVEN WITH HIM.

THE NEXT DAY AT THE COURT, HE SENT BIRBAL ON AN ERRAND. ADDRESSING THE REST OF THE COURTIERS, AKBAR SAID —

HERE IS A BASKET OF EGGS. I WANT EACH ONE OF YOU TO TAKE AN EGG AND KEEP IT HIDDEN.

LATER, WHEN I ASK YOU TO DIVE INTO THE POOL, YOU MUST PRETEND YOU FOUND IT THERE. UNDERSTOOD?

YES, JAHANPANAH

QUEER IDEAS HIS MAJESTY HAS.

BETTER HUMOUR HIM AND DO AS HE SAYS.

MUST BE A NEW GAME HE HAS THOUGHT OF.

BUT WHEN BIRBAL RETURNED TO THE COURT, THEY UNDERSTOOD.

BIRBAL, YESTERDAY I HAD A STRANGE DREAM. FROM IT I GOT AN EXCELLENT IDEA FOR TESTING THE ABILITIES OF THE MEN OF MY COURT.

ALL OF YOU MUST DIVE INTO THE POND IN THE GARDEN.

THE GENUINE MEN WILL FIND AN EGG IN IT. IF YOU COME OUT WITHOUT AN EGG, IT WOULD MEAN YOU ARE NOT RELIABLE.

AHA! THE EMPEROR WANTS TO PUT BIRBAL IN HIS PLACE.

WHAT FUN! EVERY TIME BIRBAL MAKES US LOOK SILLY. TODAY IT IS HIS TURN.

BIRBAL SAW THEM WHISPERING.

SOMETHING IS UP! I AM SURE THE EMPEROR IS UP TO ONE OF HIS TRICKS.

ONE BY ONE, THE COURTIERS DIVED INTO THE POOL.

HERE, JAHANPANAH., I HAVE THE EGG.

ME TOO!

NOW IT'S YOUR TURN, BIRBAL.

I SUPPOSE THERE MUST BE A BASKET OF EGGS AT THE BOTTOM.

WHAT WILL BIRBAL DO? HE HAS NO EGG.

SERVES HIM RIGHT. THE POMPOUS FELLOW!

HE'LL BE THE ODD MAN OUT.

COME ON, BIRBAL!

LET'S SEE YOU AND YOUR EGG.

HURRY UP, BIRBAL.

WHEN HE DIVED IN—

THERE'S NOTHING HERE! HE MUST BE TRYING TO TRICK ME.

BIRBAL CAME OUT EMPTY-HANDED FROM THE POOL.

8

AFTER SHAKING THE WATER OFF HIS BODY, HE STOOD UP.

COCK-A-DOODLE DOO! COCK-A-DOODLE DOO!

WHERE'S YOUR EGG, BIRBAL? WHAT ON EARTH ARE YOU CROWING FOR?

BIRBAL REPLIED —

SURELY YOU KNOW THAT ONLY HENS LAY EGGS, NOT COCKS.

YOU HAVE A LARGE BROOD OF HENS, HUZOOR.

BUT I AM THE ONLY ROOSTER!

THE COURTIERS FELT VERY EMBARRASSED.

HA HA! TRULY BIRBAL, YOU ARE REALLY ONE OF A KIND!

PARTING OF FRIENDS

WHY HUZOOR?

HE'S A FINE BOY.

AND SO HANDSOME TOO.

ONE DAY, WHILE BIRBAL WAS AWAY ON A MISSION, EMPEROR AKBAR CALLED HIS COURTIERS TOGETHER.

I AM A LITTLE WORRIED ABOUT PRINCE SALIM.

AKBAR INTERRUPTED —

YES, I KNOW HE IS A GOOD BOY, BUT OF LATE, HE HAS FALLEN INTO BAD COMPANY.

OH, YOU MEAN THAT BOY, YASIN?

YES, THAT FELLOW IS NO GOOD.

SALIM HAD LEARNT THE ROYAL DUTIES SO WELL.

I WAS REALLY PROUD OF HIM. BUT NOW ALL HE DOES IS LAZE ABOUT ALL DAY, PLAY CARDS, AND GO FOR SHIKAR.

YES, THAT'S TRUE. BUT HUZOOR, IT IS DIFFICULT TO SEPARATE A 16-YEAR-OLD FROM HIS FRIEND.

THAT IS WHY I AM CONSULTING YOU. AFTER ALL, AS THE PRINCE, HIS FUTURE IS YOUR CONCERN TOO.

WE WILL TRY TO FIND A WAY.

BUT A WHOLE MONTH PASSED. NO ONE COULD THINK OF A PLAN TO CORRECT THE PRINCE.

HUZOOR, SEND YASIN AWAY TO ANOTHER PLACE.

NO, THAT WILL ONLY TURN SALIM AGAINST ME.

WHY NOT TELL SALIM WHAT YOU THINK OF YASIN?

NO, MIRZA, THAT MIGHT MAKE SALIM MORE FOND OF HIM

WHEN BIRBAL RETURNED FROM HIS TRAVELS, AKBAR TURNED TO HIM FOR HELP.

YOU WANT TO SEPARATE THE TWO YOUNG MEN. WHY, GIVE ME JUST TWO DAYS.

NEXT DAY, AT COURT, BIRBAL CALLED YASIN —

BZZZZ!

ALOUD HE SAID —

NOW, DON'T BREATHE A WORD OF THIS TO ANYONE.

BIRBAL MUST BE GOING CRAZY. HE JUST SAID, "JUST ONE SEED IN EVERY MANGO."

AS SOON AS THE COURT DISPERSED, SALIM RUSHED TO MEET YASIN.

WHAT WAS IT? WHAT SECRET DID BIRBAL TELL YOU?

NOTHING. HE JUST WHISPERED SOME NON-SENSE.

SALIM WAS NOT CONVINCED.

HE COULDN'T HAVE CALLED YOU IN THE DURBAR JUST TO WHISPER NONSENSE.

IT'S TRUE. EVEN I CANNOT UNDERSTAND IT.

BUT SURELY HE MUST HAVE SAID SOME-THING.

ALL RIGHT. IF YOU INSIST. ALL HE SAID WAS " JUST ONE SEED IN EVERY MANGO?"

YOU ARE HIDING SOME-THING FROM ME, YASIN. I THOUGHT YOU WERE MY FRIEND.

OF COURSE I AM. I AM TELLING YOU THE TRUTH.

I DON'T BELIEVE YOU, YASIN.

BUT IT IS TRUE. HE SAID JUST THAT. MAYBE HE'S GOING CRAZY.

BUT BIRBAL, WHO WAS SECRETLY OVERHEARING THE CONVERSATION, WAS FAR FROM CRAZY.

YASIN, I DON'T WANT TO TALK TO YOU EVER AGAIN IN MY LIFE.

IF YOU DON'T TRUST ME, I TOO DON'T WANT YOU AS A FRIEND.

AND SOON, SALIM WENT BACK TO HIS ROYAL DUTIES.

12

THE PHASES OF THE MOON

ONCE AKBAR SENT BIRBAL TO KABUL ON A SECRET ROYAL MISSION.

BIRBAL TRIED TO MINGLE WITH THE LOCAL CROWD, BUT—

I SUSPECT THAT MAN! HE DOESN'T LOOK LIKE AN ORDINARY PERSON.

YES, THOUGH HE POSES TO BE ONE OF US, HE IS OBVIOUSLY AN OUTSIDER.

WHY, HE MUST BE A SPY.

LET'S REPORT HIM TO OUR KING.

THE KING ORDERED THE SUSPECTED SPY TO BE BROUGHT BEFORE HIM.

TELL ME TRULY. WHO ARE YOU? WHY ARE YOU HERE?

I AM JUST A TRAVELLER.

I HAVE TRAVELLED THROUGH MANY KINGDOMS AND ARRIVED HERE.

IS THAT SO?

WELL, SINCE YOU HAVE TRAVELLED SO MUCH AND SEEN SO MUCH OF THE WORLD, TELL ME, WHAT DO YOU THINK OF MY RULE?

BIRBAL PAUSED TO THINK —

YOU ARE LIKE THE FULL MOON. NO PHASE OF THE MOON CAN COMPARE WITH IT FOR GLORY.

THE KING LOOKED PLEASED. AS AN AFTERTHOUGHT, HE ADDED —

AND WHAT OF YOUR OWN KING? WHAT DO YOU THINK OF HIM?

OH HIM! HE IS LIKE THE CRESCENT MOON —THIN AND WEAK.

I AM VERY PLEASED WITH YOU. HERE TAKE THIS BAG OF COINS AS A GIFT.

THANK YOU, SIRE. YOU ARE INDEED KIND.

BIRBAL RETURNED TO DELHI. BUT NEWS OF HIS TRIP HAD REACHED THERE. AT DIWAN-I-KHAS—

TELL ME, HUSSAIN KHAN. WHAT SECRET OF BIRBAL DO YOU POSSESS?

OH, JAHANPANAH! YOU KNOW HE HAD GONE TO KABUL LAST MONTH.

YES, YES, I HAD SENT HIM THERE. SO WHAT?

BUT DO YOU KNOW WHAT HE SAID TO THE KING THERE?

WHAT?

HE PRETENDS TO BE YOUR LOYAL AIDE. BUT WHEN HE WENT TO KABUL HE DECLARED IN THE COURT THERE THAT THE KING OF KABUL WAS LIKE A FULL MOON, WHILE YOU WERE JUST A CRESCENT MOON.

IS THAT SO? I WILL ASK HIM TOMORROW IN THE COURT.

SURE ENOUGH, NEXT DAY —

BIRBAL, I HAVE A SERIOUS CHARGE AGAINST YOU.

ME, JAHANPANAH? WHAT HAVE I DONE?

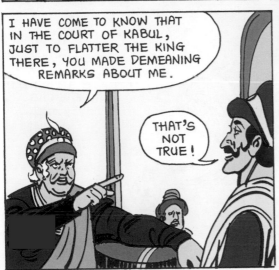

I HAVE COME TO KNOW THAT IN THE COURT OF KABUL, JUST TO FLATTER THE KING THERE, YOU MADE DEMEANING REMARKS ABOUT ME.

THAT'S NOT TRUE!

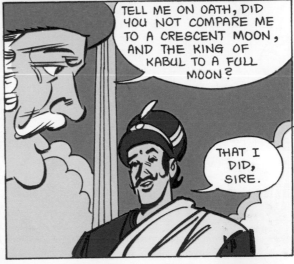

TELL ME ON OATH, DID YOU NOT COMPARE ME TO A CRESCENT MOON, AND THE KING OF KABUL TO A FULL MOON?

THAT I DID, SIRE.

HOW DARE YOU, BIRBAL! YOU ARE SUPPOSED TO BE MY MOST LOYAL AIDE.

I DID MAKE THAT COMPARISON, SIRE. BUT DON'T YOU REALISE THAT THE FULL MOON IS DESTINED TO DECREASE IN GLORY AND SIZE?

IT IS THE CRESCENT MOON THAT IS FULL OF PROMISE FOR THE FUTURE. IT WILL GROW IN GLORY DAY BY DAY. DON'T THE MUSLIMS AND HINDUS VENERATE THE MOON OF THE SECOND LUNAR DAY?

I SHOULD HAVE KNOWN BETTER THAN TO SUSPECT YOU, AS USUAL, BIRBAL, YOU WIN.

VALUE OF WASTE

BIRBAL INTERVENED —

ONE DAY IN THE COURT—

SEE THIS EXCELLENT VASE!

NO IT'S A LITTLE CHIPPED. NEVER SHOW ME ANYTHING BROKEN.

WHY, HUZOOR?

SURELY, BIRBAL, YOU KNOW THAT ANYTHING THAT IS BROKEN, CRUSHED OR ROTTEN IS OF NO USE TO ANYONE.

SOMETIMES MAYBE, BUT THAT IS NOT ALWAYS TRUE.

PROVE IT TO ME, BIRBAL.

THE JUICE WE GET FROM SUGARCANE BY BREAKING AND CRUSHING GIVES SUGAR, JAGGERY AND DELICIOUS SWEETS, FIT TO BE A DIVINE OFFERING.

THE COTTON POD BURSTS FORTH TO YIELD THE COTTON STRING. CLOTHES MADE FROM ITS SPINNING AND WEAVING ARE FIT FOR EVEN A KING.

THE ROTTEN DECAYING RAGS, OLD JUTE AND OTHER WASTES YIELD PAPER FOR THE SACRED QURAN AS WELL AS OUR PURANAS.

INDEED THAT'S TRUE, BIRBAL. EVERYTHING HAS ITS USE, EVEN THE BROKEN, CRUSHED AND ROTTEN STUFF.

THE TRUE OWNER

ONE DAY AKBAR, BIRBAL AND THE OTHER COURTIERS WERE IN THE DIWAN-I-AM. SUDDENLY —

HELP ME, HUZOOR.

CALM DOWN! WHAT DO YOU WANT US TO DO?

HUZOOR, I AM A TRADER FROM AFGHANISTAN. I HIRED A BOAT TO BRING MY GOODS HERE. NOW THE BOATMAN CLAIMS THAT HE IS THE OWNER OF MY THINGS.

THOUGH I AM A STRANGER IN THESE PARTS, I KNOW YOUR FAME AS A JUST KING. HELP ME, I BESEECH YOU, I'LL BE A RUINED MAN UNLESS I GET JUSTICE.

BIRBAL, FIND OUT THE FACTS.

AFTER BIRBAL HEARD HIS STORY HE SENT FOR THE BOATMAN AND HIS CREW.

WHY ARE YOU HARASSING THIS TRADER? GIVE HIM BACK HIS GOODS.

HUZOOR, THEY ARE MINE. HE JUST TOOK A RIDE ON MY BOAT. ASK ALL MY OARSMEN.

THE OARSMEN ANSWERED READILY.

YES, THE GOODS BELONG TO OUR SAHIB.

BIRBAL PAUSED FOR A WHILE.

WE'LL SETTLE THE MATTER HERE IN THE COURT TOMORROW.

AFTER THE COURT ADJOURNED, BIRBAL CHANGED HIS COURTIER'S CLOTHES TO THAT OF A MUNIM* AND WENT TO THE RIVERBANK WITH A FRIEND.

THERE, THE SECOND BOAT. HE IS THE MAN. LET'S GO.

AS PLANNED EARLIER, HIS FRIEND BEGAN TO NEGOTIATE.

WHAT GOODS HAVE YOU TO SELL?

OH! THE FINEST PERSIAN CARPETS.

ARE YOU PLANNING TO SELL YOUR THINGS HERE?

YES, IF POSSIBLE. I HAVE GOODS WORTH TEN THOUSAND RUPEES.

WELL, THE MARKET FOR CARPETS IS RATHER LOW IN DELHI THESE DAYS. SO, IF YOU WANT TO SELL YOUR STUFF, I'LL TAKE IT FOR FIVE THOUSAND.

FOR HALF THE PRICE?

THINK ABOUT IT AND LET ME KNOW.

WAIT! WAIT! I'LL SELL IT FOR FIVE THOUSAND.

*A CLERK

18

THE TRADER NOW TURNED TO HIS MUNIM WHO WAS IN REALITY BIRBAL IN DISGUISE.

MUNIMJI, JUST CHECK THE GOODS FOR THEIR WORTH.

SHOW US SOME SAMPLES.

BIRBAL EXAMINED THE CARPETS CRITICALLY.

LET ME CHECK THE PILE AND THE DESIGN OF YOUR CARPETS. HMM, NOT VERY GOOD I'M AFRAID.

EVEN FIVE THOUSAND IS TOO MUCH FOR THESE INFERIOR QUALITY CARPETS.

YES, YOU ARE RIGHT. WE SHOULDN'T PAY MORE THAN THREE THOUSAND.

WELL, IF THAT'S THE MAXIMUM YOU ARE READY TO PAY, I'LL HAVE TO ACCEPT IT.

AGREED. WE'LL COME TOMORROW TO COLLECT THE GOODS AND PAY THE MONEY.

NOW THE TWO WENT TO THE INN WHERE THE TRADER WAS STAYING.

I HEARD YOU HAVE BROUGHT GOODS WORTH 10,000 FOR SALE.

THEY ARE THE FINEST OF CARPETS.

WELL, THE DEMAND FOR CARPETS IS RATHER LOW. WILL YOU SELL FOR FIVE THOUSAND?

WHAAAT?!

WELL, SAY SEVEN THOUSAND! COME, IT'S A GOOD PRICE.

NO, NEVER.

NO ONE HERE WILL GIVE YOU MORE THAN THAT. THINK AGAIN.

NEVER MIND. I HAVE BOUGHT THE GOODS FOR TEN THOUSAND. I WILL SELL THEM ONLY AT A PROFIT, NOT OTHERWISE.

NEXT DAY, AT THE APPOINTED HOUR, THE BOATMAN AND THE TRADER CAME TO THE COURT.

SO, WHO IS THE OWNER OF THESE CARPETS?

I, SIR.

NO, THEY ARE MINE.

BIRBAL WAS ALMOST CERTAIN WHO WAS THE TRUE OWNER OF THE GOODS. HE SUMMONED THE OARSMEN TO THE COURT AND CALLED THEM ASIDE.

I KNOW YOUR SECRET. ADMIT, OR ELSE...

AS HE HAD EXPECTED, THE SCARED OARSMEN BLURTED OUT THE TRUTH.

YES SIR, THE GOODS BELONG TO THE TRADER. OUR MASTER GAVE US 25 RUPEES EACH TO SAY THEY WERE HIS. SPARE US!

NOW THAT HIS CRIME WAS OUT, THE BOATMAN QUICKLY CONFESSED—

YES, THAT IS TRUE. I WAS TEMPTED BY THE CHANCE TO MAKE QUICK MONEY

SINCE IT'S YOUR FIRST OFFENCE. I'LL LET YOU OFF LIGHTLY. YOU MUST RETURN THE GOODS TO THE OWNER AND ALSO PAY HIM RS. 500. TO THE STATE YOU MUST PAY RS. 500 AS FINE.

LIMITS OF LOYALTY

THERE WAS NOTHING AKBAR LOVED MORE THAN CHALLENGING BIRBAL. ONE DAY IN THE COURT —

BIRBAL, I WANT YOU TO FIND THE MOST LOYAL AND THE MOST UNGRATEFUL CREATURE ON EARTH.

YES, HUZOOR.

DON'T JUST SAY YES. YOU MUST PRESENT THEM IN THE DURBAR TOMORROW, OR ELSE...

AS YOU PLEASE.

BIRBAL AGREED TO DO AS ASKED. BUT ON GOING HOME, HIS DAUGHTER SAID —

FATHER, YOU SEEM TO BE WORRIED. YOU'VE BEEN STARING AT THE CEILING FOR THE LAST HALF HOUR.

YES, I AM A LITTLE DISTURBED.

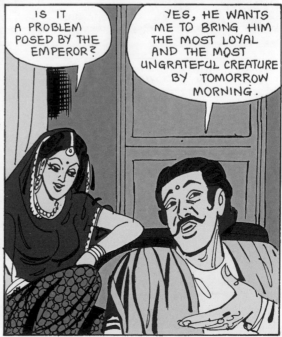

IS IT A PROBLEM POSED BY THE EMPEROR?

YES, HE WANTS ME TO BRING HIM THE MOST LOYAL AND THE MOST UNGRATEFUL CREATURE BY TOMORROW MORNING.

HOW CAN I LOCATE THEM SO FAST?

DON'T WORRY, FATHER. SLEEP PEACEFULLY. I'LL GIVE YOU BOTH THESE IN THE MORNING.

BIRBAL HAD TRUST IN THE MATURE INTELLIGENCE OF HIS DAUGHTER, AND SLEPT SOUNDLY.

NEXT MORNING—

GET READY FOR COURT, FATHER.

BUT THOSE TWO...

ALL YOU HAVE TO DO IS TAKE WITH YOU, YOUR SON-IN-LAW AND OUR DOG, MOTI.

YES. OF COURSE. WHY DIDN'T I THINK OF IT EARLIER?

BIRBAL ARRIVED IN THE DURBAR WITH HIS SON-IN-LAW AND HIS PET DOG.

WHAT IS THIS, BIRBAL? WHY HAVE YOU BROUGHT YOUR DOG? DON'T YOU HAVE ANY RESPECT FOR THE DURBAR?

ON YOUR INSTRUCTIONS, HUZOOR.

MINE?

YES, YOU HAD ASKED ME TO BRING YOU THE MOST LOYAL CREATURE.

SO YOU BROUGHT A DOG?

YES, IF YOU GIVE A STRAY DOG EVEN A MORSEL OF FOOD, HE WILL BE EVER SO GRATEFUL.

HE WILL PROBABLY FOLLOW YOU EVERYWHERE LIKE A SHADOW.

HMM. PERHAPS YOU ARE RIGHT BUT THE OTHER ONE...?

YOU MEAN THE UNGRATEFUL WRETCH. HERE HE IS.

BUT THAT IS YOUR SON-IN-LAW.

YES, HE REPRESENTS ALL SONS-IN-LAW. NO MATTER HOW MUCH YOU GIVE THEM, THEY ARE NEVER SATISFIED.

THAT'S TRUE, BIRBAL.

BUT WE MUST THEN REWARD THE DOG AND PUNISH THE SON-IN-LAW.

LET THE DOG BE FED SUMPTUOUSLY. AS FOR THE SON-IN-LAW, LET HIM BE HANGED.

BUT... BUT... HUZOOR.

NO BUTS, BIRBAL, I BELIEVE IN JUSTICE.

BUT HE IS ONLY A SPECIMEN, ONLY A REPRESENTATIVE OF ALL SONS-IN-LAW.

SO?

IF YOU DECIDE TO AWARD A PUNISHMENT, ALL OF THEM MUST BE HANGED.

WHAT DO YOU MEAN?

I MEAN, YOU WILL HAVE TO HANG ALL SONS-IN-LAW...

...INCLUDING ME AND YOUR ROYAL HIGHNESS. EVERYONE OF US IS SOMEBODY'S SON-IN-LAW.

IN THAT CASE, LET HIM GO!

AND OFF IT FLEW

AKBAR WAS FOND OF STORIES. HE COULD NOT SLEEP UNLESS HE LISTENED TO A NEW TALE EVERY NIGHT.

ONE BY ONE, HIS COURTIERS WOULD BE SUMMONED.

HURRY UP, ASIM. TODAY IT IS YOUR TURN TO TELL A STORY.

AH YES! AND THE KING DOESN'T WANT TO HEAR THE GOOD OLD STORIES. WE MUST TELL NEW TALES TO HIS MAJESTY.

ONE EVENING, IT WAS BIRBAL'S TURN. BIRBAL WOULD SPIN A LONG YARN. EACH TIME HE PAUSED FOR BREATH—

AND THEN?

ALL HE HAS TO SAY IS 'AND THEN?' IT'S MY POOR JAW THAT GETS WEARY TALKING.

I MUST CURE HIM OF THIS HABIT OF HIS. HOW CAN WE FIND END-LESS NEW STORIES EVERY DAY?

BIRBAL WAITED PATIENTLY TILL HIS TURN CAME AGAIN.

COME BIRBAL, I AM FEELING RESTLESS. TELL ME A REALLY LONG STORY TONIGHT.

BIRBAL SETTLED DOWN COMFORTABLY AND BEGAN.

ONE DAY, A RICH FARMER ORDERED A GRANARY TO BE MADE.

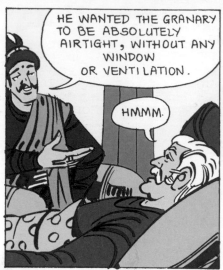

HE WANTED THE GRANARY TO BE ABSOLUTELY AIRTIGHT, WITHOUT ANY WINDOW OR VENTILATION.

HMMM.

WHEN THE WHEAT CROP WAS HARVESTED, IT WAS STORED IN THE NEW GRANARY. BUT THERE WAS ONE LITTLE PROBLEM.

WHAT?

HIGH UP ON ONE OF THE WALLS OF THE GRANARY, A SMALL OPENING REMAINED. ONE DAY, A SPARROW CAME, TOOK SOME GRAIN AND FLEW OFF.

THEN?

THEN ANOTHER SPARROW CAME, FILLED HER BEAK WITH GRAIN, AND OFF IT FLEW.

THEN WHAT HAPPENED?

ONE MORE SPARROW MANAGED TO GET IN AND OFF IT FLEW WITH TWO GRAINS OF WHEAT.

BUT WHAT HAPPENED NEXT?

BIRBAL DESCRIBED HOW FIFTY BIRDS HAD GOT INTO THE GRANARY AND FLOWN OFF.

OH COME ON! ENOUGH OF THE SPARROWS PICKING GRAIN!

BUT, JAHANPANAH, THOUSANDS OF BIRDS CAME TO THAT GRANARY. I HAVE MENTIONED ONLY A FEW. ONLY WHEN THE GRANARY IS EMPTY WILL THE STORY MOVE ON.

WHY IT MIGHT TAKE MONTHS OR EVEN YEARS TO COMPLETE THE STORY.

FORGET IT! I DON'T WANT TO HEAR ANY STORIES.

A SHARED DREAM

ONE DAY IN THE DURBAR OF AKBAR —

BIRBAL, I HAD THE STRANGEST DREAM LAST NIGHT.

WHAT WAS IT, JAHANPANAH?

WE WERE BOTH FLOATING IN THE SKY LIKE CLOUDS.

THEN SUDDENLY WE BOTH FELL DOWN WITH A BANG.

I FELL INTO A BIG PIT FILLED WITH HONEY.

BUT YOU, BIRBAL, FELL INTO A GUTTER.

HUH!

27

28

BIRBAL TURNS DETECTIVE

KALU THE ROYAL GARDENER WAS AN ABLE BUT STINGY MAN.

YOU LOOK AFTER THE ORCHARDS SO WELL, KALU.

BUT WHY DO YOU LOOK SO DOWN AND OUT?

OH! I SAVE ALL MY MONEY.

I'M COLLECTING THE MONEY FOR MY OLD AGE.

BUT WHERE DO YOU KEEP IT?

IT'S A SECRET!

ONE DAY KALU CAME IN TEARS TO BIRBAL.

OH, I'M RUINED!

WHAT HAPPENED, KALU?

SOMEONE HAS STOLEN MY LIFE'S SAVINGS!

WHAT?

I HAD STRUGGLED AND SAVED ABOUT A THOUSAND GOLD MOHURS! NOW THEY ARE GONE!

BUT WHERE HAD YOU KEPT THEM?

UNDER A PEAR TREE IN THE ROYAL ORCHARD

WHY ON EARTH?

WHAT COULD BE SAFER THAN THE ROYAL GARDEN. BESIDES, I SPEND MOST OF MY WAKING HOURS THERE.

DID ANYONE ELSE KNOW ABOUT IT?

NO, NOT A SOUL.

BESIDES I USED TO CHECK IT REGULARLY. I SAW IT JUST TWO DAYS AGO.

BIRBAL PAUSED FOR A MOMENT. THEN—

GIVE ME SOME TIME, I'LL FIND THE THIEF.

WHY SHOULD ANYONE DIG UNDER THAT TREE UNLESS HE KNOWS ABOUT THE TREASURE?

AT LAST—

AH, YES!

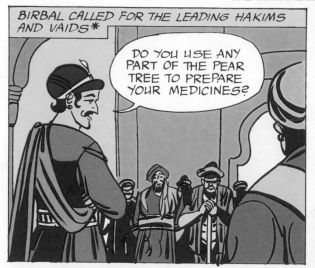

BIRBAL CALLED FOR THE LEADING HAKIMS AND VAIDS*

DO YOU USE ANY PART OF THE PEAR TREE TO PREPARE YOUR MEDICINES?

NO!

THE FRUIT IS GOOD FOR HEALTH. BUT WE DON'T USE THE LEAVES OR FLOWERS.

JUST THEN AN OLD AND EXPERIENCED VAID INTERVENED.

YOUR MAJESTY, THERE IS INDEED AN IMPORTANT APPLICATION.

WHY, JUST THE OTHER DAY I CURED A PATIENT OF JAUNDICE IN A CRITICAL STATE USING AN EXTRACT OF THE PEAR ROOTS.

WHO WAS THAT PATIENT?

SETH HAZARIMAL.

BIRBAL SENT FOR SETH HAZARIMAL.

IS IT TRUE THAT VAIDJI TREATED YOU WITH AN EXTRACT OF THE PEAR TREE.

INDEED IT IS. IT SAVED MY LIFE.

WHO FETCHED THE PEAR ROOTS FOR YOU?

MY SERVANT!

*A DOCTOR PRACTISING AYURVEDIC SYSTEM OF MEDICINE

CALL HIM!

AS YOU WISH.

YOU DUG THE ROOTS OF THE ROYAL PEAR TREE!

YES, HUZOOR.

DIDN'T YOU TAKE THE THOUSAND MOHURS KEPT THERE? FETCH THEM AT ONCE.

I I...

IF YOU CONFESS YOUR CRIME, YOU'LL BE FORGIVEN OR ELSE...

I'LL BRING THE MONEY AT ONCE.

HERE, YOUR EXCELLENCY!

YOU ARE FREE TO GO

TAKE THESE FIVE MOHURS FOR CONFESSING YOUR CRIME.

BIRBAL TURNED TO KALLI—

HERE'S YOUR TREASURE. YOU FORFEITED THE FIVE MOHURS BECAUSE OF YOUR CARELESSNESS.

THANK YOU.

IN FUTURE DON'T DO SILLY THINGS LIKE HIDING YOUR WEALTH IN THE GARDEN.